M000307000

Too many of us rush through life. We never stop to savor the moment, to ponder the lessons of the past or to consider where we're heading as we hurry from one appointment to the next. With disarming simplicity that masks a true depth of perception, Adela Amador reaches beyond the glib and the superficial to tap those deeper veins that give meaning to life. She's a natural-born storyteller, always sharply observant and inherently trustworthy, someone who can laugh at human foibles without demeaning anyone.

I'm glad we dragged her out of her beloved kitchen long enough to cast light on New Mexico and all those aspects of our culture and environment that make this such an inspiring place to live. Her "Southwest Flavor" column consistently draws more fan mail than any other department in **New Mexico Magazine.** *Readers first turned to the column for Adela's recipes, but soon they discovered she could write just as well as she could cook. What perfect ingredients for creative success, magically distilled in these heartfelt essays!*
— Jon Bowman, Editor, **New Mexico Magazine**

Nostalgic, modern, sad, happy, funny — these tales are of memory, remembrance, vitality and change. There are undercurrents, however; not all the memories are glad ones. Life was sometimes hard when Adela was growing up, but she was not one to stay behind and mope; she was far too busy for that. As she says, "We don't need to live in the past, but we need to nourish ourselves with past joys and life's richness." And so it is in this book: family, memories and culture form the background for these stories, yet contemporary life is present too. All in all a look into Adela's kitchen, and her heart.

— Dr. Tey Diana Rebolledo
Professor of Spanish, Dept. of Spanish & Portuguese
University of New Mexico

*Adela Amador's collection of stories and reminiscences is a delight. Both a participant in and a sensitive observer of the transition of Hispanic life in New Mexico between the pre- and post-World War II years, the author makes readers feel that they too are caught up in the **Undercurrents** that affected her people. Written in a deceptively simple but charming style, each story is told with a gamut of emotions ranging from joy to sorrow, from deep nostalgia to upbeat acceptance of present-day conditions. A charming narrative style adds zest and flavor to her journey of "Memories, Dreams, Reflections," as the first and last chapters are entitled.*

— Dr. Tim MacCurdy, Professor Emeritus of Spanish
University of New Mexico
author of CAESAR OF SANTA FE

Back to the future. I was taken on a poignant, nostalgic and wonderful voyage, back into the barrio that nurtured me. Thanks, Adela.

— José Armas, Ph.D., syndicated columnist

Adela Amador's collection of reminiscences and tales lovingly evokes a variety of New Mexico characters, ages 8 to 80. Her intimate feel for the land, and for everyday family life, is likewise beautifully conveyed. Whether her chosen subject be a childhood amid tall flowers or girls picking piñon nuts, the ways in which little kids can hurt each other or marriages go wrong, one is ever conscious of her unmistakable voice: wistful, bittersweet, nostalgic — yet also wise. Her side trips to Mayan ruins and to the caves at Carlsbad and Altamira further enrich this store of human experiences. And of course, we can directly savor the accounts of Adela's special and most exquisite craft: FOOD! I highly recommend **Undercurrents**.

— Dr. Gene H. Bell-Villada
Professor of Modern Languages, Williams College, MA
author of THE PIANIST WHO LIKED AYN RAND

11/23/98

Thanks Tim

Undercurrents

New Mexico Stories: Then and Now

Adela Amador

Illustrated by Claiborne O'Connor

Copyright © 1999 by Adela Amador

All rights reserved, including the right to reproduce this book or any part thereof, in any form, except for inclusion of brief quotations in a review.

Printed in the United States of America
    First Printing, 1999
    ISBN: 0-938513-27-3
    Library of Congress Catalog Number: 98-93739

    Parts of some of these stories have appeared in Adela Amador's monthly column, "Southwest Flavor," in *The New Mexico Magazine.*

    Cover photo:
        by Orlando Garcia

    Cover design and illustrations:
        by Claiborne O'Connor

Amador Publishers
P. O. Box 12335
Albuquerque, NM 87195
http://www.amadorbooks.com

Deep thanks:

to Harry, for his encouragement, support and help in the preparation of this manuscript,

to Claiborne (Mike), for her drawings and for capturing the essence of my stories,

to Zelda, for her editing help and support,

to my sons:
Orlando, for believing in me, and
Armando, for his big smile of approval,

to my sister, Eralia (Ed), for her constant encouragement,

and to the rest of my family and friends, who unknowingly supplied many of the ideas for the stories.

Other books by Adela Amador:

Twelve Gifts: Recipes from a Southwest Kitchen
More Gifts, with Variations

Other books illustrated by Claiborne O'Connor:

Twelve Gifts: Recipes from a Southwest Kitchen, by
Adela Amador
More Gifts, with Variations, by Adela Amador
The Little Brown Roadrunner, by Leon Wender
Duke City Tales: Stories from Albuquerque, by Harry
Willson
Vermin: Humanity as an Endangered Species, by
Harry Willson

Table of Contents

Memories, Dreams, Reflections

I feel that I am floating in water. But that can't be! I don't like to be in water.

Well, I do like hot water, in a washtub, yes, in the middle of the kitchen. Washtub on the floor. The water is hot, soapy and clean. I'm the first one in!

But I never liked large bodies of water. Not to get into them.

I love the Rio Grande, but I've never set foot in it.

And the ocean! It scared me when I first saw it. I exclaimed, *"¡Qué riote!"* — What a big river! They all laughed. Reluctantly I walked in and felt the sand dissolve under my feet. The waves came in and scared me. Waves have a way of beating you back, sucking you in, pushing you out.

I am a desert rat. The sand is hard and stable here, unless the wind blows. Dig your feet in the sand. Feel the grains fall off your feet, like dreams slide off the corner of your eyes at awakening.

Plants around me here grow spikes and needles to protect themselves. Our skin grows tough, too. The desert defines me.

# # #

I was one of the lucky ones.
Or was it luck?

I had the courage to change direction in mid-stream, in mid-life, and I went to the University.

There I met many important people.

Erich Fromm taught me THE FORGOTTEN LANGUAGE, the one used in myths, fairy tales and dreams.

Sigmund Freud taught me to look inside, beneath the surface of my life. I learned that what I wanted mattered, after all.

Karl Jung took me deeper into the Subconscious, especially in his DREAMS, MEMORIES AND REFLECTIONS — a wonderful book!

Joseph Campbell, in his HERO WITH A THOUSAND FACES, delivered me from traditional religious and cultural beliefs. He opened my eyes, and gave me a wider vision of life. He connected me to all the myths of all the world.

The exploring of the Subconscious told me who I really was.

# # #

I go back to my earliest memories. The oldest part of me is when I was youngest, very little. Life was hard, but I didn't know it. To me it was simply a wonder.

My mother calls it potato bread.

The fire in the *horno* is lit with tree trimmings, which we kids have gathered.

The fire is very hot.

When it dies down, my mother sweeps the ashes out with an old broom, until the floor is clean.

She tests the heat with a wisp of wool.

We children all help to bring the many pans of bread, which she places inside the *horno*.

The openings are all covered with wet burlap, and the bread is cooked for an hour.

Our reward is a roll, just as soon as it comes out of the oven.

The aroma lingers in our minds.

Though she is long gone, my mother's life continues to be touched by memory.

#

My mother was milking the cow in the shed at home. She always took one of us with her to the barn to do the toting and carrying. Isn't that the way it works? The helper works harder then the professional!

The tree stump which she used for a stool wasn't in its place, so a bucket turned upside down did the trick. She couldn't find the rope to tie the cow's legs and tail, so she used the next best thing. Off came her flimsy half-apron, which she twirled around a few times and used in place of the rope. She sat down to milk without hesitation.

Being the scaredy-cat that I was and thinking that all big animals such as cows and horses could and maybe would eat me up, I stood at a respectable distance and wondered if all was safe. I questioned the strength of the flimsy apron/rope and Mother said, *"La vaca sabe*

que está atada." [The cow knows she is tied.] I still
don't know exactly what she meant, but adults are not
very patient with children's questions and concerns.
However, I've thought about this since then, and have
noticed the difference between a domesticated animal,
like a cow, and a wild animal, like an antelope or a
deer, which would never permit an apron string to
restrain them.

# # #

I remember hiding in a flower garden as a child. The
magic, beauty and fragrance remain with me to this
day. The flowers were standing tall, making a kind of
statement. They included cosmos, Chinese sunflowers,
delphiniums, dahlias and hollyhocks. They were just
the right height for a small child to walk gently under
and among those stalks and into a make-believe world
of her very own. I remember sitting in the middle of
the aromatic blossoms.

We lived miles from the closest town, where my
father was a caretaker for his uncle's sheep ranch. My
father had built a house and five enormous barns, dug
wells and built water tanks for the sheep and for home
use. It was a God-forsaken place called El Solo, which
means "all alone." My young mother had planted the
flower garden, simply by scattering seeds all around
the house, no doubt trying to beautify a small space.
She felt surrounded by the most dismal, barren
landscape anyone could imagine.

The workmen had built a fence around the house to

keep the animals out and the children in. So the garden was my playground. I watched the seeds sprout and grow; I enjoyed the flowers and anything that moved in that magical world. The beauty of butterfly wings delighted me and I sat in this magic underworld and felt perfectly safe.

The area was rocky and many snakes had been found there, and I had been warned about them. But warnings don't work well with a small and curious child. One day I found a little rattlesnake. I poked it with a stick and it hissed, so I teased it some more. I don't know how long I played with my new friend! When my mother found out who my playmate was, she whisked me away and into the house and killed the poor little snake with a shovel. I felt bad about that.

Even today, I watch the birds go in and out among the flowers in our garden and I'm glad they let me observe them at close range. I can still imagine all kinds of magic activities that grown-up humans aren't aware of, taking place in those special hiding places. What a wonderful world!

# # #

As a child I did not like onions. My mother used too much onion in absolutely every meal she cooked, I thought. So *posole* was not my dish, the way she made it — until one day she sent me to take a pitcher of posole to the neighbor. The day was hot, and as I wandered away, barefoot, I looked for a shady spot to while away the time and rest. I stopped beside the

Presbyterian Church, under a weeping willow tree and put my feet in the cool ditch water that was gurgling by. I carefully placed the pitcher so it wouldn't spill and removed the top to see what was inside.

It reminded me of popcorn. I took a kernel and ate it, and found it good. I took some more. Soon I found a piece of meat, which was rare in those days, and the eating became more interesting. I must have been hungry, because I ate my fill and found it very good.

But I knew I had done the wrong thing. I continued on to the neighbor's and when she uncovered the dish, she scolded me for having stuck my fingers in the food. I handed her the pitcher and took off running, not wanting to hear her, feeling guilty, and knowing the story would get back to my mother anyway. But I learned to like posole!

#

Once my older sister tried to get out of the chore of making tortillas for my father's lunch bucket by complaining, "I can't get them round." It does take practice!

My father persuaded my sister to try again, telling her, *"No entran rodando. No ruedan. Tienes que mascarlas."* ["They don't roll in. They don't turn like a wheel. You have to chew them..."]

I remember how as a little girl I used to swipe a whole tortilla while my sister was making them, dunk it in the bucket of fresh clean water that was standing there, scoot to the sack of sugar which was intended for canning, dip the tortilla in and flop it over, plastering both sides with sugar — and then run out and hide somewhere until I ate it all! I really wanted more sweet than was around.

# # #

I remember as a child a very special meal of corn on the cob, home-made butter and tortillas and milk. When the sweet corn was ready, there was plenty of it. There were many of us, so the pot must have contained at least three dozen ears! We were told to fill up — no one was worrying about a balanced meal! It was "all you could eat," which was a little rare. We filled up with what there was, and called it a wonderful treat.

# # #

There was a man in our village who in his own stern way planned an evening of fun for the children, while he got his work accomplished. His family and ours would easily come up with ten kids to work. On a moon-lit night he had us over for a husking party, with a surprise at the bottom of the heap of corn. The pile was so high we felt we'd never get to the bottom. But, as the adults told stories of ghosts and witches, time went by fast, and the corn was husked.

In our perverse way we liked the ghost stories, because they had magic and suggested some pretty awful things which we had not thought of. One time the boys in the village went up the hill and set fire to a tire and rolled it down into the arroyo, while we were husking corn. It frightened us and thrilled us, and we never doubted, at that moment, the existence of ghosts.

The ghosts were usually friendly, but a bit scary, as they could turn up anywhere and the moving shadows on a moon-lit night convinced us they were really there.

When the husking was almost over we could see that a big watermelon was our surprise. And it didn't take long for us to devour it. Then the neighbor immediately sent us home, saying it was past our bed time. It had been that for a while, but he made sure the work was done before he let us go.

# # #

I remember one time, visiting my grandmother, I went up the hill to a tiny one-room building with her. She went to sweep and dust the little room. I can still see this tall, stern, stately woman, wearing an apron with her hair covered with a rag, sweeping the dirt floor. We didn't talk at all, but the clear impression on me as a small child was that this little room was Grandpa's house and that Grandma lived in the big house down the hill. It was much, much later that I figured out that the little building was the local *morada* and that my own grandfather had been a *penitente*.

# # #

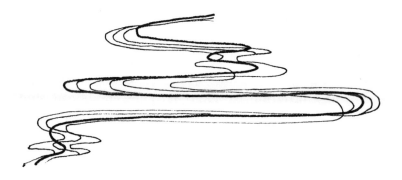

I shift from memories of my own childhood, to my two little boys, and their own sense of wonder, as they began their lives in this world.

# # #

My older boy had a favorite book, which he carried around with him to see who would read it to him. There were so many in my family that it was read many times a day. Soon he memorized it and some of the adults were amazed, thinking he could read, because he turned the pages at the right time. Of course, the pictures helped him do that!

With the book in his hand he asked Granma if he could read to her. She said, *"¿Qué lees, Hijito?"* [What are you reading?]

He answered, *"Jaque en el Binestaque."* He thought he had translated the title into Spanish. Well, titles are difficult to translate, and he did his best!

# # #

I remember when Grandma gave my younger little
boy a toy corncob pipe. He was told that he had to
keep it in his pocket, when he was at school or church.

Christmas was coming, and he and three other six-
year-old boys were assigned a recitation in the
Christmas program at church. They practiced and
learned their parts well. They each had four lines to
memorize and say, and together they told the story in
poetry form of the birth of the Christ Child.

When their turn came, they marched up to the front
of the little chapel, and stood in a straight line. My
little one was to recite first, but when he faced the
congregation, he became speechless and forgot every
word.

He stared at all the people and when they began to
smile and snicker, he placed his hands on his hips and
stated, "That's what I hate, when people laugh!"

He took out his corncob pipe, placed it in his mouth
and walked off stage. The other three performers
followed him, without a word. End of scene!

# # #

I remember how my boys faced winter, compared to
when I was very young. While I was growing up, we
lived on a farm and had plenty of fresh fruit and
vegetables in summer and fall, and canned or dried
fruit and vegetables in winter, with milk and eggs year
round. Our cereals were cream-of-wheat and oatmeal,
usually, but when things were really tough, we ate
bran out of the same sack that was being fed to the

cow. Ours was toasted in the oven and was really very good with fresh milk and honey. Our home-made bran was not much different from the "hi-fibre" products we're supposed to buy and eat today for our good health.

Times changed. When the father of the family has a steady job, the people consider themselves "middle-class" or even "affluent." Some of us fell into this way of thinking. We went through a stage of eating what the T.V. suggested, instead of the good old basic foods. In the mornings, my boys ate cornflakes or some other cold cereal according to the jingles, drank their glass of milk at my insistence, and then trotted off to school, all bundled up as if they were in Alaska in mid-winter.

At school they noticed that some of their playmates had no coats — some didn't even have sweaters — yet they suffered little from the cold. When my children told this, my retort was that those other kids were eating a substantial meal of beans and tortillas before school, and that kind of eating kept them warm. By mid-morning my cornflakes boys were famished and needed a treat, while those other little stomachs filled with beans and tortillas were satisfied until noon.

# # #

The two little boys want to go fishing.

They are not aware of all that that entails.

They have watched men catching fish on T.V. and want to do the same. They think they'll get a fish every time they cast.

Their father orders two complete fishing outfits for them through THE READER'S DIGEST.

The three of them go to a small stream nearby, but hooks and lines spend more time caught in trees and bushes than in the water.

The boys' father takes us all north to Rodarte, to fish. There's a nice wide stream there and a small reservoir. The boys try their new equipment, such nice rods and reels and special line, complete with hooks and sinkers and everything. Nothing happens!

A little country boy, a native of the village about ten years old, comes by with a hook at the end of a string tied to and old willow branch. In no time he has caught a fish!

My boys marvel, and make friends with the stranger and talk with him about fishing. Before he leaves, he gives them the fish he caught.

The boys wonder aloud, to their father — maybe they have the wrong equipment! "Shouldn't we have just a string with a hook, on a home-made willow pole?"

Times change. One of those boys now keeps our family freezer supplied with fresh trout. The other tests the "quality waters," every chance he gets. That's where the fishermen have the fun of catching really big ones, but release most of them, so the fun can continue. My boys have come a long way from where they started, in the fishing game.

# # #

I see two little boys, maybe four and six years old, in their bib overalls, jumping up and down with glee, at the prospect of feeding two little orphaned lambs. Their father fills two bottles with warm milk, tightens the nipples and hands one to each boy. The lambs run toward them, knowing what's coming, since they have been fed this way before.

At first both lambs try to suckle from the same bottle, leaving one neglected child on the verge of tears, and the other boy overwhelmed. Their father separates the lambs, so that each boy has one lamb to feed. Finally each lamb finds one nipple and sucks hard, bumping its head against the boy's belly, as they would their mother's, in order to bring the milk down. They back the boys against the wall of the building. The boys can be pushed no farther, so they feel more in control of the situation.

Each boy holds a bottle tight against his belly, while a lamb drinks. Soon one of the lambs pulls the nipple clear off the bottle and milk spills out all over. Both lambs are slobbering all over the boys, butting them in the *panza* (belly), trying to get back to their source of food. The spilled bottle is refilled, and it all ends well. The boys are hot and sweaty and stand between tears and laughter, joyous, a bit scared, but proud to have succeeded in feeding them.

# # #

I remember picnics. Our extended family was very large, so the mountains were the best place for the whole tribe to meet. There were often five or six of us siblings with our families, and that meant ten or twelve kids at any time.

The children literally went wild. They ran up and down the mountainside, often scraping knees and rolling in the dust like little pigs. Then they were in the stream, shoes and all, after placing watermelons and cans of drinks in the water so they would be cold when needed.

Naturally there were accidents. You can't have a bunch of kids feeling the freedom to run unrestrained without someone getting hurt. One of the cousins, while picking wild strawberries, was hit on the head by a stone rolled down by kids playing higher up the mountain. My two-year-old swallowed a piece of bark, and turned blue in the face. My mother removed it from his throat with her forefinger. She was used to taking care of emergencies and never hesitated to do what needed to be done.

This kind of thing made my father very nervous. Each time some accident happened he said we should have stayed home, where we could get to a doctor if need be. I never understood why he said that, since his own twelve children never ever saw a doctor while growing up. I think for him things were simply changing too fast. He made us all laugh once. "The bathrooms are now inside, and these picnics make you cook outdoors, the way man did thousands of years ago. That doesn't make sense!"

And those were the days when changes were few and gradual. Now that I also can't keep up with the pace of change, I understand him better.

# # #

In English we say it's raining cats and dogs, or even pitchforks and hammerhandles, but in Spanish our proverb says, *"Llueve sapos y culebras. "* [It's raining toads and snakes.]

A tourist asked the New Mexico oldtimer, how much rain we get here in the desert. The old man answered, "About seven inches a year." Then he scratched his chin and stared off at the distant mountains and said, *"Sí,* and I remember last year — I remember the afternoon it came."

That would happen in July, with those hot days, cool nights, and every now and then, rain by the bucketful. It's possible to get two or three inches of rain in 15 or 20 minutes, once or twice a year. I remember looking out the back kitchen window, towards the Sandia Mountains, seeing water spread across acres of land, looking much like a flowing river. We had just received as much rain as I had ever seen at one time.

The damage was incredible. We were in the middle of adding several rooms to the house. Unfinished adobe walls melted down, and window openings allowed the unfinished rooms to fill with water, destroying building materials and everything else inside. Brush, weeds and whatever the water gathered along the way plugged the culverts, causing the water to rise out of the arroyos and cover the fields and roads, damaging crops and causing more destruction.

But after that rain an incredible thing happened. The lawn was filled with tiny frogs. My boys were ecstatic! They ran for their little red wagon and tried to fill it up with frogs, but as fast as they put them in the wagon the frogs jumped out. The children continued their attempt to get a wagon full of frogs, until darkness came, the day ended and two tired and disappointed boys went to bed. Next day there were no frogs to be found anywhere. The boy's questions were not answered and neither were mine. We wondered where they came from, where they went, and even whether they were frogs or toads, that is, *sapos*.

# # #

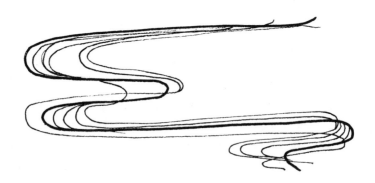

My father taught us to live in harmony with nature, as much as is possible, but from time to time things happened which made it all feel like something of a struggle. Nature could be generous, but sometimes it seemed there was something going on which made it hard, almost hopeless. I'm remembering things that happened.

At one time my husband and I were almost self-sufficient on our small plot of land. We grew most of our fruits and vegetables, raised chickens and rabbits and had our own bee hive. We were careful to harvest the rabbits at the correct time, and there were always frozen rabbits in the freezer. Of course, there were always losses. Once the cage door was left open carelessly and rabbits escaped and were never found. More than once, on the coldest winter nights, stray dogs came looking for a warm meal. They found it, after damaging the hutches badly.

One time, a bull snake got into the cage through the small openings in the chicken wire side wall, and after swallowing several baby bunnies, found himself too big around the middle. He couldn't get out. You can guess what happened to that unlucky visitor!

Humans came once and destroyed the hutches more efficiently than stray dogs ever did. They hauled away two dozen live fryers.

# # #

One time we thought we would raise our own turkeys and have them throughout the year, not just at

Thanksgiving. We ordered a dozen chicks. When we
arrived at the depot to pick them up, half of them were
dead. The six that were left were frail and sickly
looking, but farm people are used to reviving animals,
so we fed and cared for them as best we knew how.

We learned a lot about turkeys! They are helpless
and stupid. When they fall on their backs they kick
their feet up in the air uselessly. They will lie there
and die of hunger and thirst, unless you get them on
their feet again. If they happen to be caught out in the
rain, they stand and get soaked and often die of cold.

By November we had only two turkeys left and
were glad we had that many. But that isn't the end of
the story. One cold and windy evening a few days
before Thanksgiving, I was on my way to check the
animals before dark, when I heard a commotion in the
chicken coop. I ran up to the area and saw a fox with
one of our turkeys in its mouth. He looked at me. I
started running hoping to scare it, but it only turned
and trotted off, uphill.

I was angry and started crying, which made it
harder to run against the wind. The fox ran, I ran, I
had to stop and catch my breath, the fox stopped and
looked at me as long as I wasn't running. Did I intend
to wrestle him for the turkey, or what? I had nothing
in mind beyond hoping that he would drop it and go.
Perhaps I was ready to snatch it from him, if I could
get to him. When I realized I had lost the struggle, I
went back home angry and very disappointed.

# # #

One time my two boys became aware that the chicken coop was full of fresh feathers and they wondered if a skunk or some other animal was coming in, when they weren't looking. They became more watchful, and later found a half eaten chicken. All the time they were watching on the ground for a four legged animal and never suspected what it really was — a sly old hawk. She was quietly sitting on a perch near the ceiling of the coop, waiting for the right time to pounce on her prey. Finally the boys spotted her and closed the door to shut her in the coop. Then they wondered what to do.

My youngest, about eight years old and the more fearless of the two, ran down to the house to get his BB gun. BB's didn't faze the hawk, so between the two boys they decided to get the .22 and really take care of the problem. They couldn't open the door for fear the hawk would fly out. They got on the roof and through a big knot hole shot and killed the culprit.

I do not remember where I was at the time, and even now it scares me to think about it. I can certainly understand how easily accidents happen with firearms. Of course, the eight year old became the hero of the story, much to the dismay of his parents. The boys no doubt felt that they had to protect the animals, but now I feel that they were too young to have felt such responsibility. Then, again, maybe that's what makes for responsible men later in life.

# # #

Picking piñon is almost a work of art among the natives of New Mexico, and was a family affair in my childhood. I remember several times when we went out to pick the little nuts, we were not always successful.

On one occasion, in October, or maybe early November, we piled into the school bus, which our father drove. We packed water, food and bedding, and headed north toward the Santa Fe National Forest. We arrived in time to find trees with nuts under them, eat a bite and settle down for the night.

We were so excited to be there, full of great expectations for the next day. Early in the morning we awoke to a white world, and our precious find of piñon nuts was covered with six inches of snow. We left empty-handed. I remember my father had trouble getting the bus started in the cold.

Another time we went picking not far from home. The sun was shining brightly and we found the most beautiful big, brown piñon nuts all over the ground. Each of us had a small can to fill, but we kept running from tree to tree, always looking for greener pastures, or in this case bigger piles of nuts, stepping over the best crop, and getting ourselves full of pine pitch.

I was very young, and remember finding a beautiful white velvety animal, the size of my hand. I was fascinated and forgot all about the piñon. I wanted this new-found friend all to myself, and I wanted my father's permission to take it home.

He seemed quite alarmed and wouldn't hear of it. He taught me that it was an albino tarantula spider and that it could bite. I think my father thought it was poisonous, because he wouldn't let me touch it. I also learned the meaning of the word "albino," which he said was a lack of normal coloration of the skin, and that sometimes it happened even to people. For a long time after that I kept checking faces, hoping to find a person really white and velvety, like my little friend, the tarantula.

# # #

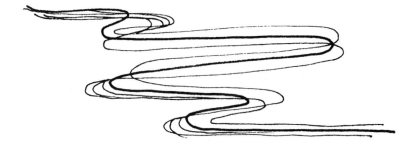

The struggle with nature never seemed as discouraging as the unavoidable incidents of fighting with our fellow human beings.

# # #

Noise
Talk, talk, talk
Roof-brain chatter
Meaningless words, which we have heard before —
Why repeat them?
We need to hear our own voice, to prove to
ourselves that we are alive.
Noise on the freeway, like a storm at sea —
Meaningless noise, called "music" —
boomboxes disturb my thoughts while stopped at a
traffic light.
Lurid so-called "news" repeated day and night —
Pictures shown over and over, which will determine
what the politicians want as outcome —
Shopping centers filled with noise —
Songs we don't want to hear —
Christmas music cheapened —
Piped-in music at the dentist's office, so loud I can't
think or read —
"Music" over the phone, as I wait for the right
person to come listen —
Planes overhead, sometimes so low I have to duck
—
The garden gives me peace.
Crickets chirping, frogs croaking, finches singing,
doves cooing —
Nature is kind and restores our sanity.
Nature gives us pause; gives us peace.

# # #

Dreams
I don't live my life by dreams,
But I welcome them when they come.
If not written down the minute I wake up,
they disappear like messages written on blowing sand.

I try very hard to collect my thoughts, and think
things out, but the thoughts get out of my head and
rest on my scalp.
They stray among objects in the room.
Around the lamp and on the shelves overlooking the
books — up the stairs they go and out the door.
I fly out of bed and follow them and I see the
danger they are in.
They seem to follow a certain noise.
In and out of traffic, under cars, between the
wheels, and then they are gone.
I follow the noise and find them in a yard full of
dogs barking furiously.
I'm afraid the dogs will trample my thoughts or
swallow them, as they bark.
Somehow the thoughts wiggle out of danger.
I hear an awful noise, but find only misty images in
my brain — no thoughts.

# # #

There has always been much fighting about
irrigation water. One time when my father was out of
the village, which happened often as he went where his
job took him, my mother was trying to irrigate the

garden. The water was being cut off by a mean old neighbor. He did not like the idea of being told by the ditch-boss when to irrigate. My mother's garden was above stream from his, so she had the water first in the afternoon, once every eight days. Each time she opened the gate he came and closed it and cut her off.

She sent me to watch, but what could a little kid do? I was afraid of the old man and never said a word to him, each time he cut her off. The third time it happened, my mother sent me away to watch the water and waited for him at the main ditch. He came. With a shovel in her hand she commanded him to stop. He pretended not to hear. She looked him in the eye and said, "Not another step, or this shovel will break your head!" He stopped cold, turned around and never bothered her again. She was a small woman, but she never made an empty threat.

# # #

We have all heard the phrase, "shrieking like a fish wife," but I never knew the source of it until I traveled to Asturias, in the north of Spain, in the fishing port of Gijón. Coming down from our "pensión," looking for what we'd call breakfast at home, we stumbled on an incredible scene. I thought "fishwives" were simply women who sold fish, or fishermen's wives, but we found this group of women at the front end of a line of people, where they had gathered to meet the fishing boats as they came in. They were ready to buy the fish that they would later sell. They literally attacked the fishermen, claiming they had been promised the catch, and grossly abused each other, arguing over the best and biggest fish. The shoving, scratching, screaming and cussing created a scene like I had never seen or heard in my life, and I think of it whenever I buy fresh fish.

# # #

My oldest brother remembers that he was ten or eleven years old when he went one time with Dad up the mountain to get wood. When they got up there, my father said to him, "Son, we have come for a turkey, not for wood, because tomorrow is Thanksgiving Day." Soon a flock of wild turkey flew from the bush and my father shot and killed one. My brother does not remember what happened next, but I do. I was sixteen years old at the time.

They came home about dark and instead of rejoicing over the successful hunt, there was whispering and secrecy, which I didn't understand at all. We took the turkey down into the cellar, where the only entrance was through a door in the kitchen floor. My mother heated water on a wood stove and handed it down into the cellar, so we could pluck the turkey. My father explained that it was unlawful to kill wild life without a proper license; therefore, we were not to tell anyone that he had killed a wild turkey. He explained that if found out, he could be fined heavily and maybe even imprisoned.

It was difficult to keep such secrets in a village

where large families were sustained by wildlife.
Naturally we told the other children at school, and they
told us similar stories. Our turkey was bigger, or their
deer had more antlers, and so forth. I think the Forest
Rangers kept away from isolated villages during the
Depression, because they knew the natives were
surviving off the fat of the land.

# # #

The late 60's, and the war goes on.
Sad and frustrated, he comes home from college,
Fearful that his number will come up.
He knows that he doesn't want to die!

Father and son are miles apart in their thinking.
One is patriotic, and does not question why.
The youth is thoughtful,
Convinced the war is wrong, evil, uncalled-for.

The headlines are mere numbers,
Casualties from both sides.

"Well, that's not too many," the father says.

"But, Dad, they're dead!
Their life is gone, forever!"

# # #

A Visit Too Long

When Grandma wrote and said she was coming over to see them, the children were excited, but not for long. The sleeping arrangements were being changed around and someone would have to sleep with her. At first all the children volunteered, but when they saw her, they were intimidated and one after another refused the honor.

Grandma was tall, thin and a rather good-looking woman when she smiled, but most of the time she reminded you of the woman in the picture by Grant Wood, *American Gothic* — stiff and stern! She had white hair and blue eyes and flaunted her Spanish heritage, while discriminating against her grandchildren's Mexican background. One often heard her calling the children, using disparaging names. *"¡Ven acá, Negra!"* [Come here, Blackie!] *"Esta fea no viene, cuando llamo."* [This ugly girl doesn't come, when I call.] To her, pale was beautiful and good, and dark was ugly and bad.

Is it any wonder that her daughter had managed to move many miles away from the constant reminder that she had married a dark-skinned Mexican? The distance was great and the families seldom visited each other. That was good for all concerned, because the

27

visits were usually painful for all.

The three girls were all under twelve years of age
and their little brother was only a few months old. The
girls were full of fun, always laughing and in motion.
Their young mother had been able to put up with all
their doings, because she had gotten used to them one
by one, as they came along. The grandmother did not
know how to cope with the noise and confusion of all
the children. She sometimes felt their whole purpose in
life was to terrorize the adults. The mother handled
them by more scolding and being more strict than
usual, trying to please and appease her own mother.

There was turmoil in this household, but the children
found ways out of their misery. They found hide-outs,
determined to get out of the adults' way and avoid
doing chores. They closed the door to their own
bedroom, or they ran outside and climbed the apple
trees. In spite of Grandma's way of being, there were
always things to laugh about.

The slamming of the screen door bothered the
adults, but they didn't think of unhinging the spring,
which made the door close with such a bang. The
oldest of the girls figured it out and unhooked the
spring and soon the banging as well as the screaming
stopped. The flies and the little mongrel dog, who was
not allowed in the house, now had the run of the place.
The screen door stood open most of the time and the
adults were too busy visiting to notice.

The house was silent. Either the girls were being
good or they were up to something bad. When the
adults checked, they found the dog in bed surrounded

by the girls, looking at a Christmas catalog. The kitchen door stood wide open, and flies were all over the kitchen table.

After a severe scolding the girls were given a couple of fly swatters and ordered to kill all the flies. They swatted right and left and at each other, squealing all the time. It became a game, which did not accomplish the job. Grandma was very unhappy, and grumbled about the girls' worthlessness and their inability to do anything right. The girls paid no attention to Grandma's disapproval. It seemed to go in one ear and out the other.

No one knew how long she was going to stay, but the children thought it had already been an eternity. They retaliated by pouting and asking their mother in audible whispers, "When will Grandma be leaving?" The mother shushed them, asking them to be nice. There seemed to be no date set so far. The girls turned away disappointed, and conferred together about how they could annoy Grandma enough to get her to leave.

The summer days were hot and the house had no fans. Often the old lady went out under the trees, either to darn socks or crochet. The children scattered, keeping their distance from her. The dog settled nearby in the shade, to keep cool. Grandma didn't like dogs, and if this one came too close, she kicked him away. Poor dog!

Grandma caught a very bad cold and was in bed several days, which gave the girls a break. When she recovered and joined the family again, she seemed strangely distracted, forgetting many things. Her

constant question was, "Where are my glasses?" even when she had them on. The girls thought this was pretty funny. Instead of telling her kindly that they were on her face, they laughed and ran out the door.

At night they could hear Grandma's stomach growling and making all kinds of noises, which provided more reason for laughter and making fun. One said, "She must be hungry."

Another said, "She can't be hungry. She ate everything!"

The day came at last, when someone was coming to take Grandma home. She arose early, placed all her clean clothes on her bed, while she took a bath. When she went to her room to dress for the trip, her girdle was missing. How would she ever hold her stockings up! She was sure she had put it on the bed. When she couldn't find it, she was furious and assumed that the girls had taken it for spite. They denied it and were as puzzled as the adults. The two grown women looked everywhere — in vain. They finally found two old pieces of elastic, and sewed a homemade pair of garters.

When she left, Grandma did not bother to say goodbye to the girls, or even to thank her daughter for her stay. The children were delighted that she was gone, and as a matter of fact so was their mother.

The disappearance of the girdle remained a mystery all through the winter. In the spring, when the girls' father was cultivating the strawberry patch, in order to mulch it with straw, the cultivator turned up the girdle. The little dog spotted it as soon as it appeared in the garden. He ran and grabbed it immediately, as if it was his own. It had been buried all winter! He may have buried it for spite, because the grandmother hadn't treated him any better than she had treated the girls. The dog didn't like Grandma either!

# # #

Clean Kitchen

One of the teachers from the prestigious boys' school where my husband taught invited us to a pot-luck dinner at his home, together with some other faculty members. One of the couples was the school counselor and his wife.

I had been divorced and recently re-married, and felt very insecure as a faculty member's wife. It was a very difficult time in my life and their conversation, so drenched in academia, was of little interest to me. I was the only native in the group, I was not a teacher, and I did not really feel included. I had problems of my own and not much time for their meaningless patter.

After a while I noticed the conversation had shifted to the subject of food. My contribution to the meal had been a large pan of beef stroganoff. I chose it very purposely, hoping to avoid any stereotypes about Mexican food. It didn't work! I had used the recipe from *The Joy of Cooking,* just in case anyone asked. The stroganoff was indeed delicious, but not a word was said about it.

The conversation went from Italian food, to Russian food, to Chinese food. Then someone mentioned New Mexican. Suddenly the counselor's wife, whom we shall call Beth, announced in her good old Texas drawl, "Mah daddy says Ah cain't cook good Mescan food, 'cause my kitchen's too clain!"

I was literally horrified. There was complete silence, and I couldn't believe that no one, not even my husband, had come to my rescue. Was she really saying that good Mexican food could only be made in dirty kitchens? My mouthful of food stuck to my throat and all I wanted to do was first kill her for insulting me and then run away from this alien bunch of insensitive people called educated humans. As soon as the meal was over I picked up my empty pan and we went home. My poor husband caught hell all the way and for some time to come, for not speaking up in my defense.

At another faculty party, I heard Beth tell the same stupid story again. She undoubtedly thought it was a good joke, since no one had called her down on it. Once again there was silence, but I guessed she was just too dumb to notice that no one was laughing.

During the holidays I was giving a little party and didn't know just how to keep from inviting Bob and Beth. I thought for a long time and decided to call Bob and have a little talk with him. After all, a counselor should be aware of such things, even if they are very close to home. I told him about the party and how I wished they would come, but I did not want Beth telling her joke one more time. She had insulted me and the rest of the natives and if she did it one more time in my presence I would be forced to ask her to leave my house.

He pretended to have heard the story for the first time, and apologized. He seemed honest enough and even had her call me to say how sorry she was and that she was not aware of having insulted me. Tell me, how ignorant can a person with all those academic degrees be? Do we really learn anything in school? They did not come to the party, and I must admit I was glad. Soon after that incident, they left the school. I never knew exactly why.

# # #

Fly, Fly Away

I have heard the lady say that she cannot understand why the Good Lord made flies. I could ask the very same question, wondering why He made humans. We are all born, we eat, we drink, we die.

I guess they call us "flies" because we fly. But they don't call the man "walks" because he walks or the woman "sits" because she sits all the time. We don't understand them any better than they understand us.

I fly into the room and find the man hunting around for his glasses with a book in his hand. She is sitting in a chair reading, as I buzz around the room in a wide circle, looking for a place to deposit my eggs. They both immediately stop what they're doing and take after me, as if I were the Enemy. I settle in a window behind the metal slats of the blind, and they go back to their reading.

I wait a while, hoping they have forgotten all about me. I fly toward the light and get inside the lampshade. She immediately picks up the smasher and clobbers the shade, trying to get at me. I fly through the top of the shade and land on the man's candybar. He doesn't notice, so I enjoy a morsel and take off before they spot me. I fly down the stairs into the basement, just to try my wings. I enjoy the fact that I can fly, and think of my wings as my greatest asset.

Time goes by and I forget all about them and fly upstairs again. I buzz around a little, and there they are, eating something from small little dishes, something which looks and smells very good. I need to taste it, but am not sure how to do it without being chased away first, and maybe hit with the smasher. She thinks I've gone away, because I'm half hidden in a fold in the drape.

When they become involved in loud and rapid conversation, I fly into the dish of goodies to take a bite. It is quite delicious.

The lady sees me and is horrified and grabs the dish and dumps the contents into the garbage bag in the large basket by the stove. She begins screaming about how dirty flies are. What she doesn't know is that I have just washed my feet, rubbing my forelegs together at the rim of her drinking glass. I also sucked up a nice drop of water to quench my thirst. When she finishes her lecture on dirty flies, she takes a nice long drink out of the same glass where I washed my feet.

She's still screaming. "We fight and fight, and they keep coming! Where do they come from? Where do they breed?"

The man answers, "I think they hatch somewhere down in the basement." Well, I could tell them! The compost pile that he's so proud of, with the scraps from the kitchen, and the chicken manure he hauls in, and the crap he gathers from the stray dogs that visit the front yard, and all the families of cockroaches and roly-poly bugs — it's a great place for breeding.

Soon the battle begins again. I fly down the stairs and they follow me, acting crazy, swinging the smasher in the air wildly as I fly past them. I hide in a dusty bookcase and after a while they give up, thinking I am dead.

When all is quiet, I fly back up into the kitchen and find a lovely piece of cooked but cold cow meat. Usually such things are covered up, but they forgot, chasing me downstairs and up with the smasher. I ate all I wanted, laid a few dozen eggs in a crack between the fat and the meat, and planned to come back later. The lady leaves her easy chair to answer the phone, so

I wash my greasy feet on another drop of water on the rim of her drinking glass.

In the Spanish language they assume that we are all females, and call us *moscas*. They call our little cousins *mosquitos,* as if they were all male. Isn't that crazy? In the English language they assume that we have no sex at all and call everybody, male and female, "flies." This little poem about another batch of cousins of ours came from one of the more thoughtful of them. They aren't all stupid after all.

> And here we have the bounding flea —
> You cannot tell the he from she;
> But he can tell,
> And so can she!

# # #

Lady Luck

Ramón's few acres were watered by a mountain stream, which made farming possible and even enjoyable in the peace and quiet of the valley. There were no cars, no airplanes and no neighbors. He tended his farm and took care of his animals, which provided him, his mother and his spinster sister a simple living. If the mother or sister had to be transported, he used the horse and buggy. He preferred to go alone, when he could use his horse and saddle, which were his prize possessions and personal transportation.

The past week-end had gone by as all week-ends went for Ramón. He went down to the *cantina* to drink beer and listen to his friends tell the same jokes, the same stories he had heard all his life. He was a quiet, simple man in mid-life, who listened but never said much.

The evening lengthened into night and José, the bartender, wanted to lock up and go home. Poor Ramón was too drunk to mount his horse but someone helped him as always. They lifted him into the saddle with difficulty, then slapped the horse on the rump, and sent him on his way.

The horse knew the way home, for he had taken this

same route many times before with a semi-conscious rider. Once he arrived home, his sister ran out and helped him off the horse, into the house and onto the cot where he slept. The horse remained saddled, standing outside until next morning, when Ramón was sober enough to tend to him.

Lying on a cot by the fireplace, and listening to the crackle of the cedar wood, he wondered about many things. Would his life be different, if he had a loving wife and children who cared about him? Why had he not married his one and only school chum, with whom he had enjoyed talking and dancing in his early years? He had waited too long to pop the question, and another less shy young man had taken her.

He wondered how he got home the night before. He remembered having bought a raffle ticket with his last dollar, but he couldn't be sure what they were offering as a prize. "I could have bought myself another drink or brought home a sample bottle for my cure this morning," he thought to himself.

The first drink of water in the morning was always the worst. He wondered what rotten food he had eaten. Better to blame the last bite than the last drink.

Just then his mother came into the room, angry as usual, because of his drinking. He didn't offer any excuses anymore, or even listen to the sermon, for it was the same one he heard the last time and the time before that.

He tried to recall the happenings of the night before and what the raffle was all about. Could it have been that beautiful rifle they had on the counter? No, they wouldn't raffle something that useful! "Wouldn't it be great, if I had a new rifle!" he thought. "I'd go hunting and get us a small deer for Thanksgiving dinner. Then both my sister and mother would be happy with me." Once again his thoughts went back to a family of his own.

The day was cloudy and dark. Maybe it would snow. He got up and took care of the horse, unsaddling him, watering and feeding him, and putting him out in the pasture. He fed the chickens and hogs and then was glad to get back inside the house. He built a big fire in the fireplace and since the women were not speaking to him, he went back to his cot and slept for hours.

He thought he was dreaming, but as he listened closely, he realized someone was knocking loudly on his door. He lived several miles from the nearest town and seldom did anyone come around and least of all on Sundays. He opened his door and was quite surprised to find José, the owner of the bar, standing there. What could have happened the night before to occasion this visit? Ramón knew that in his stupor of the evening, he could have done most anything. Then he noticed that José had a rifle in his hands. He was struck with fear! But José smiled and said, "You won the raffle!"

Ramón was totally speechless. When the truth hit him, all he could say was, "¡Cuando a uno le toca, hasta por la chimenea entra!" He meant that when Lady-Luck smiles on you, even if you are drunk as the dickens, good luck comes in through the chimney.

Ramón had many more adventures like this. Often he

went to the *cantina* of an evening or week-end, intending to have just one *cerveza* to quench his thirst, and head for the hills where he lived. Why it never worked out that way he never understood. If he could only drink that way, there would be peace at home and he would not have to hear all that damn sermonizing that his mother was so good at.

This time he would not stay any longer than it took to drink one *cerveza*. The fellows were joking and talking about the village girls and it was fun listening to them. He had one drink, then two and before the third drink was gone, things began to get blurred and the talk no longer interesting. He could think of only one thing, a place to lie down, and it could be most anywhere. At first the fellows included him in their conversation, but once he got drunk, they left him alone.

One of the guys had a guitar, and soon they were singing and carousing as if it could last all night. José had a young wife waiting for him at home and was anxious for them to leave. He waited till midnight and started putting things away, letting them know it was time to close bar. He noticed that Ramón was fast asleep on one of the booths. It was the same old story every time! José woke him up and told him it was time to go home.

After rubbing his eyes and stretching a bit, Ramón went out on his own, but not too steady on his feet. The rest of the fellows delayed a bit, poking fun and laughing at poor Ramón.

Ramón wandered out into the night, not really

knowing what he was supposed to do. All he wanted
was to sleep it off. He tried to mount his horse, but
each time he tried the horse moved a little and Ramón
fell off.

He was getting very tired and since the horse was not
cooperating, he tried the door to one of the pick-up

trucks parked there. It was either too hard to open or locked, so after many tries, he managed to climb into the back. Now, that was a great place to sleep! No one would bother him there.

Some time later the bar emptied out and the guys got in their pick-ups and headed for home. The last one to get going was José, who noticed that Ramón's horse was still tied to the post where he had first seen it, when he parked his truck. He thought for a moment, but then figured that Ramón was probably behind the bar taking a leak. José was a little drunk and too sleepy to give it much thought

The following morning, José got up very early so he could water his alfalfa before the sun got high up in the sky. He made some coffee as quietly as he could in order that neither his wife nor the children wake up. He got himself a hot cup of coffee, got in his truck and sped down the highway. All of a sudden he saw in the mirror a man rise up in the bed of his truck! He slammed on the brakes, spilling hot coffee all over his pants. The jerk nearly broke the man's neck. José jumped out of the truck to see who the hell the man was, only to find it was his friend, Ramón.

"What the hell are you doing here in the pueblo this early in the morning?" he demanded.

Ramón's thoughts were all jumbled and he was having a hard time figuring out why he was there. It dawned on José what had happened, before Ramón was able to reconstruct the previous day's happenings. "You mean to tell me you left that poor horse tied all night without water and food? He should kick the hell out of you," José said. Ramón was used to being scolded, and had no reply. "Come on in the house and I'll get you some coffee, so you can sober up."

Ramón jumped down from the bed of the truck and made a face which indicated that he was experiencing extreme pain. Poor guy, he had lain on a wrench all night and his shoulder felt as if broken. He rearranged his shirt and shook the straw, manure and dirt off his clothes, angry and disgusted with himself, but speechless. His mouth tasted like shit and he really needed a bath, clean clothes and food, but most of all, he needed a drink for the cure.

José was annoyed that now he must take Ramón back to the bar instead of doing his work before the heat of the day. Nevertheless, he was good-natured and decided to cook some breakfast for both of them. Soon the whole family was up and enjoying breakfast, sharing their food with Ramón. It occurred to him that he could do the same with friends, if he had a place of his own.

Lady-luck was with him once again, providing breakfast, a ride home and this lovely feel of family. Ramón became sharply aware that he did not have a wife and family, only his mother and sister, who were really more pain and trouble than fun. He thought how nice José's arrangement was, and for an instant he resolved never to drink again.

But, he thought, "Oh, if I could only have one more cerveza!"

# # #

I'll Do It If It Kills Me

It was a working man's town, when there was work to be done. The sawmill employed several men, but only when orders came for one hundred boxes or more, and once the orders were filled the men were let go. The railroad also employed a few men, hired to load and unload freight. The train came in only twice a day, so the men worked only when needed. The rest of the time they tended their gardens in the summer and cut wood and fed the fires in the winter.

Reading, writing and arithmetic were taught in the little one-room schoolhouse. Those subjects were of little interest to the children. The boys sat at their desks and dreamed of all the fun things they could be doing, if they could only get away. They wondered why they went to school at all. No one forced them really, but it was a place to meet their friends and plan the after-school games. There was little else to do. Once there in school, they had to stay until the teacher dismissed them.

Juanito was a seven-year-old, spunkier than a billy-goat, and he was sure that he could do anything that the older boys could. He went everywhere with the gang of older boys and was accepted by them, because he was such a daredevil. He often said, "I'll do it if it kills me!"

The boys were chased from the river by any adults who saw them there, because the water ran swiftly and there was danger of drowning, or going down in quicksand. But danger was just what they liked. The boys tried playing at the railroad yard, but if the men were there and saw them, they chased them away. The big problem was where to play. The town did not have a single grassy field or a playground, so the children spent their days playing in the dirt, and looking for excitement.

It was almost Christmas and Juanito wanted a bicycle more than anything in the world. The family was very poor but he was their only child, so the father thought there must be a way. The older boys also hoped he would get a bike, so the little rascal could go with them wherever they went and try all the tricks they tried. The father was able to buy a used bicycle. He fixed it and painted it, so it looked pretty good. Juanito was pleased, and became more daring that ever. "I'll do it, if it kills me!" he cried, as the gang challenged him in a hundred ways.

On a certain day after Christmas, Juanito and three other older boys, none older than ten, waited until the train had passed through and the men had been dismissed from work. Then they ran into the railroad yard to play. Who knows what they had in mind! They ran to and fro chasing each other under boxcars that were standing in a siding. Then they found some huge logs piled neatly by the fence. Maybe they wanted to see how fast and how high they could climb on the pile of logs. Maybe they liked to hear the rumble as a log on top broke loose and tumbled down, providing the excitement they wanted. Who knows? For a while all went well, and they had lots of fun.

No one in the town was aware of what they were up to, for the evening was cold and the folks were inside their houses waiting for their dinner. Juanito with his short legs was having a difficult time climbing to the top of the pile, but he was determined. Suddenly the whole pile came loose, and half a dozen of the huge logs were dislodged and came rolling down with a roar. The boys on the ground yelled and clapped their hands at the show. They were completely unaware that Juanito had disappeared underneath the pile of logs.

It took the grown men of the town hours to move the logs, one after another, like a game of giant Pick-up Sticks. But it was no game. At the bottom of the pile they found Juanito's crushed little body, with a look of surprise on his face.

The boys heard his voice, in their memory, "I can do it! I can do it! I'll do it, if it kills me!"

# # #

Temor

"Please come home early tonight," Rita begged. "I get awfully scared when the baby coughs so much. He nearly chokes with the phlegm."

Carlos looked at her, got himself another cup of coffee and said nothing. Silence was his game and he played it well. He had never committed himself to anything in the time they had been married.

She often wondered if this was all there was. She questioned what she was getting out of this marriage. Of course, she had these three beautiful children — two little girls, three and four years old, and a three-month-old baby boy. They were her whole life. Every day she took care of them, kept house and waited for Carlos to come home from work.

He worked as a foreman at the sawmill and was well paid, but Rita couldn't tell what happened to the money. The couple never went anywhere and never had anyone over to their house. He trusted no one. From work he stopped at the *cantina,* had one drink, or more, and played cards with the other workmen. He never talked to Rita about his work or his drinking and gambling habits. He never discussed his family or his work with his drinking companions. They called him *"Silencio."*

This night was different from all other nights. Rita

was afraid. The baby's cough got worse, and she had to hold him upright all evening, so he could dispel the phlegm and not choke.

She looked out the window every few minutes to see if she could spot Carlos on the path coming home. The night became pitch dark and very windy, and with every noise the wind made, she trembled with fear.

Finally the girls fell asleep and Rita was grateful, for now all her attention could go to the sick child. She considered going to call Carlos, when and if the child went to sleep, but hesitated because she remembered that long ago Carlos had told her never to go to the bar after him.

Fear is a strange thing. One fear can challenge another. Fear makes you take chances you would otherwise not take.

After several more bouts of coughing fits both she and the child were completely spent. Rita decided to go after Carlos.

She settled the child and ran out the door toward the bar. It was a short distance, but between the dark and the wind she felt it was taking her forever.

The wind blew the bar door open and slammed it with a bang, as she entered. Every face at the poker table turned around to glare at her. In a fear-filled voice, Rita said humbly, "Carlos, you must come home at once. The baby is very sick. He is choking to death!"

Carlos turned towards her, pushed the cards away, stood up slowly, and without a word followed her out the door.

Rita knew he was very angry, and she started running down the path. Suddenly she heard a shot. She stumbled and fell, feeling a sting on her arm. As she tried to get up, she heard another shot ring out. She couldn't imagine what was happening. "Who could be shooting at us? And why?"

She heard the men from the bar calling Carlos' name. They came running toward her. Some of them helped her get up and walked her toward her house. "Where is Carlos?" she asked.

One of the men said quietly, "He's gone."

"Where did he go?" she asked. "Doesn't he know that someone shot me?"

The man answered in a kind voice, "Carlos shot you, and then turned the gun on himself. He is dead. I'll go get you some help."

The commotion woke the baby and he immediately started coughing violently. How could she possibly take care of him, with all these new problems? She sat at the kitchen table, unable to imagine taking care of herself, let alone anyone or anything else. She held her left arm with her right hand, and the blood ran down her fingers, and at the same time she heard the child still choking.

Reluctantly she went to the crib, picked up the child, held him to her chest and patted his back, trying to relieve him of the phlegm. She stuck her finger down his throat and pulled out a gob of phlegm. Both she and the child were smeared with her blood.

The kitchen door stood open. Rita heard noises and excited voices out there in the dark, but she couldn't pull her thoughts together. "Why? Why?" was as far as she could get.

The man's wife came in and took the child from Rita's arms. Soon another neighbor came and without saying a word washed her arm and bandaged it. In the silence Rita came to understand the whole tragedy.

Carlos was deep in gambling debts, and her appearance at the bar humiliated him greatly. All that triggered his pent-up anger, and caused the shooting. His intent was to teach her a lesson, but when she fell, he thought he had killed her, so he turned the gun on himself. No doubt he assumed that would cancel all his debts.

Carlos's body was never brought to the house, even though that was the custom in the village. There was no mortuary, so he was laid out in the school house. They would bury him outside the church cemetery, because a suicide could not be buried in "hallowed ground." "Such foolishness!" Rita thought. "But they can do as they wish. I will not be there."

Rita remembered old stories that had to do with Death. They now flooded her mind and left her unnerved. There was the idea of someone being buried alive, of a corpse being found later turned over inside the coffin, a voice heard calling after the coffin was sealed —

A great deal in life is mysterious, and it is not the dead but the unknown that is so horrible. Rita knew that superstition was the offspring of undeveloped intelligence, but shutting her eyes tight didn't dispel the fear which terrorized her.

The nights were long and sleep was far away. Every noise was magnified and ghosts were everywhere. Better to get up and do something. She took the clothes basket and went out into the night to hang diapers on the clothesline. She kept looking all around her, expecting someone or something to happen.

The more she tried to dispel gloomy images, the more haunting they became. A cold chill ran down her spine. She felt someone or something pulling back her long loose hair. She felt someone breathing heavily over her head. As she ran to the house, she thought it was silent Carlos, trying to take her with him.

Rita bolted the door and left the kitchen light on. She crawled into bed, pulled the blankets over her head and shut her eyes. She was too nervous to remain there for long.

Overcome with terror she got up and lit a candle in front of Our Lady of Guadalupe. She knelt to pray, making the sign of the cross. No words and no thoughts came, except the same superstitious nonsense that kept creeping back into her mind.

The church bell chimed the hour — six o'clock in the morning. She had not slept at all. The bell sounded mournful and depressing. The girls woke up and needed attention. She was glad. She would have to leave attempts to pray for some other time, and tend to life itself.

#   #   #

The Test That Failed

She sat alone in an old rocking chair on the back porch, wondering back through the years. Clara did not know if she was young or old, even though they had just celebrated her eightieth birthday.

She looked back on her miserable life and tried to understand it. She was trying to heal herself, but there were too many memories that could not be changed. Her life was too nearly over.

Clara was the oldest girl in a very poor, large family. Food and clothing were hard to come by. She was all of fifteen years old, when she first heard her parents discussing her future. Every now and then a letter came in the mail and both parents read it very carefully, after the children were ordered out of the room, or put to bed. Her marriage was being arranged, and she had no idea even who the young man was. The most important thing in that family was to marry the daughters off as soon as possible in order to have someone else feed them. Both sets of parents undoubtedly knew each other or why would they be corresponding? The letters went back and forth for a long time.

One day after a letter arrived and was read several times by her parents, she was called and informed that

they had received very good news from some friends.
They had a son who wished to marry her. She was
very shy and did not know how to respond. They
explained that there would be a wedding and Benito
and she would become man and wife. In a way, this
was unthinkable! How and why would she leave her
home, her parents, her brothers and sisters and go far
away to live with a man she did not know? Her
questions indicated how backward she was then and
what little she knew of life.

Her father had moved them all to a small Mexican
village, made up of just a few families, who didn't like
newcomers, or even each other. Clara was part of a
large family, completely isolated from the outside
world, and her father's strongest wish was that they
not marry one of the village boys. She wondered what
he knew about that community that made him feel that
way.

The main social affair in that village was weekly
church services on Sundays. Neither of her parents
were dedicated to regular worship, so they seldom
went. Her father wanted the children to go to Sunday
School, but not for the Christian teachings. His real
reason was so that they would learn to read and write
Spanish, which was the language used in that
missionary church.

Every once in a while there was a dance, but the
girls were seldom permitted to go, because a dance
would expose them to the village boys. As a result the
girls grew up extremely naive and over-protected.
What could they possibly learn from the outside world,

when they had no contact with it?

The more talk there was of the marriage the more excited Clara became, not really knowing what it all meant. She had learned that marriages were arranged in other parts of the world, such as China or India, but how could it possibly have happened to her? she wondered. Finally the date was set and more letters came and went, but none of the letters were for her. Everything was being arranged by the adults, and what she thought of the whole thing never came up. Her wishes were never considered, and if they had been, she would not have known how to respond. Looking back later, she wondered, was I innocent or just plain ignorant?

Two weeks before the wedding she and her mother went north about a hundred miles, to her grandmother's hometown, not far from the prospective groom's family. Her grandmother and aunts all gathered to prepare for the wedding feast. They made cakes, pies, *biscochitos* and many other goodies, and stored them in a large trunk, where the mice could not get at them. During the last two days of the visit, they killed the fatted calf, plus many rabbits, and chickens in preparation for the big occasion. The church had announced the wedding for a whole month, so they knew that people would come from miles around.

Clara's grandmother made the wedding gown. There were many horse-and-buggy trips to the only Mercantile Company for miles around. The store was poorly stocked, so they made do with whatever was available. The grandmother decorated white satin fabric with cheap narrow lace and sewed blue ribbons into tiny flowerets, embroidering each center with pale yellow thread. She sewed each flower onto the sleeves and torso of the gown. It was not really very expensive, but nevertheless Clara thought it was the most beautiful dress she had ever seen.

The young couple met the day before the wedding. There they were, two bashful young people seeing each other for the very first time, one day before becoming husband and wife! They stared at each other speechless. What could they say, for they knew nothing about each other? They were young and attractive, but they couldn't think beyond that day.

The wedding events were exciting! The gathering of the families and neighbors, the food, the church ceremony, the music and dance — Clara had never attended an event like this before, and here she was the center of attraction.

But once it was over, reality hit her square on the face. She went to live with her husband's parents, which was customary in those days. She found out that it was no fun at all. Benito's mother and Clara did not like each other from the very start. There would never be a woman good enough for her favorite son, the mother thought, and there was no love lost between the two women.

Everything Clara did seemed to be wrong, and the mother-in-law knew no nice way to teach her without making her feel stupid. Her favorite way of humiliating her was to laugh her witch's laugh and tell the relatives and neighbors how dumb Clara was. The poor girl cried herself to sleep every night, and Benito could not understand why Clara did not like his mother.

Fall came too soon and the old woman announced that it was time to butcher a calf. Any change seemed like fun to Clara, after the monotony of everyday life. Little did she know that this little incident would provide the test which the old woman needed to prove Clara's lack of ability as a young wife. She stood around waiting to be told what to do, and since everything was new to her, she had a feeling that the old woman had a trick up her sleeve.

When the stomach and entrails were emptied into a bucket, the old woman handed them to Clara, together with a small paring knife. "Go down to the river," she said, "and don't come back until both the stomach and tripe are perfectly clean!"

She laughed and told the neighbors how she had always hated that job, but that now she had a slave to do it for her, meaning Clara. The superstition was that since Clara would be unable to do the job, the two women would never get along and the marriage would be terminated.

Little did Clara know that part of the stomach was made up of many, many folds which resembled the pages of a book. It was called *librillo* from the Spanish word for "book." Another part of it is called the honeycomb, because of the thousands of tiny compartments which make up the stomach wall. Both *librillo* and honeycomb must be scraped to remove the inner lining. If any of the inner lining is left, there will be a very unpleasant taste in the resulting dish, which

was called *menudo*.

As Clara worked with the tiny paring knife in the ice cold water at the river, she recalled an incident from long ago, when she was still very young. Her mother had been called away, just as she had started to pluck a chicken for dinner. She left Clara with the job, but did not tell her to plunge the chicken into boiling water before plucking. She tried to pluck the feathers with cold water and finally ended up crying herself sick, because it was an impossible job. Now she was asked to do a similar job, away from family and under frightful circumstances.

She worked for hours, with that tiny paring knife, in the ice cold river water, while the old witch laughed and told neighbors that the job could never be done. To everyone's surprise, the stomach was scraped clean. It seemed only a miracle could have done it. When Clara presented the job to her mother-in-law, the old woman was dumbfounded. Clara received no thanks, no praise or comment of any kind.

Even though she passed the so-called test, her marriage was a tumultuous one, and after many years of suffering it ended in divorce. Clara often wished that it could have ended sooner than it did! Husband and wife never did learn how to talk to one another. Whenever he wanted advice or needed to share something with someone, he went to his mother. Clara always felt left out, for years and years.

The children were very much like their father. Their lives were tragic, from Clara's point of view. John left for the service at the age of seventeen and never came back, never wrote back, and was never heard of again. Their older daughter died in a car accident on the night of high school graduation. The younger daughter was the silent one. She never shared her thoughts and dreams with anyone. One day she left home, supposedly to visit someone, and she never returned.

Years later, Clara rocked on the porch, remembering. She knew that she no longer believed in that superstition. She knew that the test had failed. She accomplished the impossible task of cleaning that calf's guts, but nevertheless her *suegra* and she never got along.

Clara thought of this tragic life of hers, and wondered if things would have been different, if she had had a chance to grow up and make some choices for herself. Maybe not. But at least she would not be so angry now and feel so damn cheated!

# # #

Undercurrents

Many years ago there was a village on a hill overlooking a deep canyon, where the river stumbled over boulders. It created deep holes and secret areas where fish escaped the swift waters only to be caught by youngsters with a willow, a piece of string and a hook.

The small farms in the valley below were irrigated by the ever-flowing river. The cattle grazed and thrived on pastures there. Beans, chile, squash and other vegetables grew well, plus wheat and corn, which were ground into flour at the mill up the river.

As the children grew up, they left the village to find employment elsewhere. Some married and came back to what they remembered as a romantic place of their childhood dreams. There they learned that you can't go home again. Trying to make a living on the farm was very different from growing up on one, when the parents were responsible for success or failure. Those who had become accustomed to a factory pay-check while away found farming very uncertain.

Only five families remained in the village and two of them were old couples who had never left the land and knew nothing of the outside world. The remaining families were young and had small children. The siblings and cousins played together, seeking adventures, unhampered by restrictions or adult interference of any kind. With no traffic and no one who would or could possibly harm them, they felt safe in their little paradise.

The Lunas had four little girls. Carmen was twelve years old, Marta was ten, Eva was eight and little Rosita was six. Carmen had learned to swim with her older cousins and loved the water. Usually the adults took them down to the river once a week during the summer. This year the adults had been very busy with the garden and it had been several weeks since they had been down to the river. The children were bored, and knew that only an afternoon playing at the river could make them happy.

It was early July with blue cloudless skies, and a perfect day for fun and frolic. Carmen begged her mother to let them go down to the river to play. She promised to take care of the girls and especially little Rosita. After a lot of begging and arguing the mother consented. The older ones were to play in the shallow water away from any deep holes, and Rosita was to stay out of the water, playing on the grassy slope.

Down the path they ran, betting who would get there first, quarreling over every little thing as children often do. It was nothing serious, just enough to make life unpleasant for each other. Once they arrived, they ran into the water and splashed each other and screamed as the cold river water hit their sun-soaked bodies. For a little while Carmen remembered her mother's warnings, and they gave her a chance to be bossy with the others, but the instructions didn't stay in her mind. She soon forgot everything except having fun.

Her plan was to teach Marta and Eva to swim, so they could impress the cousins the next time the families got together. She taught the two how to float and then a few strokes and soon forgot that Rosita was even there.

The little girl played her own games. First she rolled on the grassy slope and little by little into the shallow water. She stood up. No one noticed or scolded her for going into the water. It was fun to take little steps, farther and farther away from the river's edge. She felt very grown up. Suddenly one more step took her into the swift current and she was swept away like a leaf. No one noticed!

It was quite a while before the girls noticed she was missing. Carmen realized what had happened and panicked. She jumped out of the water crying and screaming, hoping someone would hear her anguished call. Her winged feet took her up the path with her long black hair flying away from her face. Tears clouded her vision. She felt she was hardly moving. The distance and the roar of the river drowned the sound of her voice, until at last she reached the top of the hill.

Her mother was the first to hear her cry and knew instantly that something horrible had happened. The villagers listened to the story, told incoherently with sobs and gasps, and without waiting for all the details, the men flew down the path to the river. There they confronted the dreaded truth. Rosita was gone. The women and children ran to the ridge of the hill and stood speechless, watching and waiting with fear and anticipation. The men found Marta and Eva sitting on a boulder, staring into the water, as if they expected Rosita to come out any minute. They seemed to have no understanding and no explanation as to what had happened. There was only stunned silence and grief.

The water was very swift, and though the men ran down the river's edge, they came to no trace of Rosita. Some of them followed the stream for seven miles, all the way to the closest town, and there they alerted the people so that they too could help in the search. Days went by with no success in finding Rosita, and the people's sorrow was doubled for the lack of a burial.

The mother felt guilty, for letting the girls go to the water, and she sensed disapproval in the neighbors, even though they said nothing.

Carmen felt guilty, and it was made worse at school in the fall. "You let your little sister drown," one boy said with a sneer.

Guilt and blame ricocheted from one head to another. The screaming lasted only one day. The crying went on for weeks and months. The silence, the worst accuser, came and stayed.

# # #

Brujerías

The youngest child had been crying all night.

"How can I rest and be ready for work in the morning when I can't sleep? Yesterday I nearly fell, while spreading the hot tar. It's dangerous going up and down the ladder when I'm always tired."

"I'm so sorry," Emma said apologetically, as if it were her fault. "He cries day and night, because he is hungry, and then he cries after I feed him because everything I feed him makes him sick. He is so small and so thin for a two-year-old. I don't know what to do."

Juan got up and went for a cup of coffee. When he returned, Emma continued talking. "My *comadre* says he is *embrujado* and that we must see a *curandera*. She knows La India María, who lives in the pueblo. Maybe she could help us. What do you think?"

"I don't believe in this thing called the evil eye, but I'm ready to try anything. I can't remember when I slept the whole night through!" He raked his fingers through his hair and grumbled more.

"It's not the baby's fault. The only thing which seems to help him is hot tea, *te de hierba buena,* with a little honey."

This and similar conversations were repeated over

and over, and always came to an abrupt end. Neither
parent knew what to do and both felt guilty for their
inaction.

The couple lived in an isolated town of only a few
families. The village had no telephone; the roads were
bare dirt, and among all the families there were only
two cars and one old battered pick-up truck. Necessity
made them good neighbors; they shared what they had
and trusted each other. They were all aware of the joys
and sorrows which were part of their daily life.

One day the *comadre* came over to see how the
baby was doing, and found Emma crying and trying to
rock him to sleep. They talked of taking the child to
María, but they were afraid of having car trouble on
the way and ending up stranded. The *comadre* decided
to go alone and try to convince María to come to
them. After she left the couple tried to figure out how
to pay María.

The family had a small farm with a few farm
animals and a small orchard. At this time of year they
had ripe apples and pears — surely this was enough to
barter with. That's how business was done in this
village, where there was no money.

María did come, and they were glad to see her. She
was a large woman with a commanding voice, and
seemed a little brusque, because she was all business.
She entered the house and asked to see the child. After
a short conversation with Emma, she spotted her
eight-year-old daughter, Raquel, who stood by. "Go to
the chicken house and get me an egg," she ordered.
The child ran out as commanded and returned soon

with an egg in her little hand.

In the meantime, María placed the baby over a blanket on the kitchen table, and took his clothes off. With the diaper she made a circle around his umbilicus. When Raquel brought the egg, María broke it and emptied it over the baby's belly button. He winced and let out a surprised cry. María studied the egg, muttering all the while, as she moved the yolk with her finger every which way, as if looking for something. No one understood her words, or saw what she saw. After a while she pulled out a hair and claimed that it belonged to the person who had caused the *brujería*.

She assured Emma that the baby would be all right, but told her not to nurse him any more. She also told her not to give him any milk unless it was goat's milk.

The baby slept all night, and so did the father! The next morning over breakfast, the parents didn't know quite what to think. The baby was still sleeping, and the parents were both rested.

A couple of years later Raquel ran into trouble at school. She had always enjoyed her classmates and they had good times together. Suddenly something strange happened at recess. She found the other girls whispering to each other, looking at her from across the yard. They began to exclude her from games and conversation. Raquel felt completely alone and couldn't understand what was happening. Finally one of the most outspoken of the girls said to her, "Your mother is a witch! Your mother is a witch!" The others

chimed in with, *"¡Tu madre es bruja! ¡Bruja!"*

The words hurt her. Raquel's eyes filled with tears. She didn't know what to say or do. At first she yelled back, "You must be crazy! My mother never hurt anyone!" The taunting continued and Raquel ran home to tell her parents. She could not understand the unexpected turn of events, even though her parents could. Raquel refused to go to school the next day. She hoped it was only gossip, which would go away.

Her parents knew that Emma was being accused of having bewitched a friend of hers. A couple had moved to the village the year before, all the way from Italy. They were different and didn't fit in with the other villagers very well. Emma had befriended the wife, even though no one else in the village did. The woman was sickly and medicinal herbs didn't seem to help her.

Often Emma and Juan visited them and helped them with farm work. Emma used to take food, including soups and baked goods, because the woman could no longer cook for herself and her family. During the past winter Emma and Juan saw very little of the other family, because the distance was too far to walk in bad weather.

The following spring the woman was very ill, and her husband spread the gossip that Emma had bewitched his wife with the food. The village had heard it all. Raquel was the last to know.

Juan and Emma discussed it with each other and with Raquel. Emma cried. "I've lost a friend, and the village hates me and is afraid of me."

"This whole *brujería* business is nothing but stupid superstition!" Juan exclaimed angrily. He turned to Raquel. "Pay no attention to those crazy girls. It's meanness! The woman was sick when she got here, and they have to blame it on someone. There's no such thing as a *bruja*!"

"What about the time La India María came and cured my little brother?" asked Raquel.

"It wasn't eggs and hair and witchcraft which cured your little brother," Juan declared. "It was good advice about what to feed him. He was allergic to your mother's milk, and cow's milk. When she stopped feeding him that, he got well."

They talked until late, and Raquel felt better. But she wondered if she'd ever have any friends in the village again.

# # #

The Convent

After months of war in Europe, finding a piece of New Mexico land to call my own was in a way a dream come true. While I was away, my father had exchanged my team of horses for six acres of land in a lovely valley, far from where I had ever lived. In a short time I learned that establishing a home for my growing family was very difficult, and a far cry from what I had expected. I was faced with three great problems: finding a place to live, finding a job, and deciding where to send the children to school in the fall.

There were no houses in the village which we could rent, while I built one for us. We were forced to live in a two-room shack, which leaked like a sieve. The only dry place was under the kitchen table, where the children liked to play, building dams and ditches to water their make-believe gardens in the dirt floor. An unusually rainy season welcomed us and made our lives quite miserable. In later years I found the area to be very dry, and often wished for all the rain that I cursed that first summer.

I found a job in the sawmill in a town seven miles away. The trip was difficult on a dirt road. We spent a cold and wet winter, while I worked at the job, and built three sturdy rooms for the family on our own land.

The public school was two miles away, which was too far for my little ones to walk. What were we to do? The neighbors spoke to my wife and me about a convent, "a very good school," they said, which was in the same town with the sawmill. But the nuns would not take day students. My little girls would have to board there. I would have to take them in on Sunday night and bring them home on Friday after school. My wife and I did not like the plan at all. The children would be away from the family too much of the time, but we had no choice.

My own father's parents were products of the Mexican Revolution, and had strong negative feelings toward the Catholic Church. Those same feelings were imbedded in me. My wife's attitude was similar because her entire family had been excommunicated from the church for having sent their son, her younger brother, to the only high school in the area. It happened to be a Protestant missionary school, and that was a no-no in those days.

Nevertheless, we spoke to the nuns and they seemed to be agreeable enough, so we decided to put our two little girls in their care. We had not brought our children up Catholic, and that made all the difference, it turned out, in the way they were treated. The nuns made them feel inferior.

One of their favorite sayings was: *"Está Pedro muy viejo para cabrero,"* [Pedro's too old to be a goatherd], meaning my girls were too old to learn anything important. They had not been drilled in the Catholic faith early enough. They didn't know the prayers and the gestures used in prayer. It was very strange to them, even though the nuns seemed to think it should be something very natural.

The children hated school from the very beginning. Sunday was the saddest day for them, and tears flowed easily. They seemed to be learning little else but prayers, how to be good Catholics, and what was needed in order to get to heaven. When I picked them up one Friday, my little one said to me, "I don't want to go to heaven. I want to go home, and stay there!"

The other child said to me, "Are there nuns in heaven? And where is heaven?" They were very good questions, I thought, and I had no answers.

The whole school seemed to pray all the time, and the children thought the prayers were long, repetitive and boring. The nuns were disappointed with my children for their lack of interest in the prayers, and tried to fill the girls with guilt and shame for who they were. The children told us stories, which we could hardly believe, until we checked them out.

On Monday morning at breakfast, the children were given a bowl of oatmeal, enhanced with a little sugar, and a large tablespoon of castor oil. The nuns, and many others in those days, believed that a weekly purgative was necessary to keep one healthy. If the children did not eat that ugly mixture for breakfast, it was saved for their lunch. If they didn't eat it then, it was saved for dinner, at night. If a child threw up, more castor oil was added to the oatmeal. My little one said to me, "I try to swallow it before I taste it, but when I close my mouth, it comes out my nose."

The children were punished for not knowing the required prayers. Often they were made to stand in the corner of the classroom, holding a heavy book over their heads. It was very tiring for little girls. They stood there crying, while others recited their lessons. Punishment seemed to be the norm, no matter what they said or did. In the night, if they had to go to the bathroom, they were punished with more required prayers. If they needed a drink of water, more punishment resulted, and more meaningless prayers.

The children told us of their nightmares, which consisted of ghost-like figures walking in the dark, murmuring repetitive prayers, and always giving or receiving more punishment of some kind.

How many times does a person have to repeat something, before it is accepted? Is Someone deaf? Was all that vain repetition really devotion? Or was it guilt, or simply force of habit? Perhaps all three...

We finally promised the children that they would not have to return to the convent after Christmas. Other arrangements were being made. During the time they were there, their tears nearly drowned us, and we were sorry we had ever exposed them to such abuse. The idea of children in a convent gives me the shivers to this day. Now, from my own experience, I think my father's assessment of such things was correct.

# # #

Beauty and the Beast

As a young girl I remember my mother wearing a black dress much of the time. At first I didn't understand why, but was told that it was a way of showing grief for the death of her brother. It was called *luto* [mourning]. Black was worn for a whole year after a family member died. If another member died before the year was up, the time began again. Therefore, some women seemed to be in black forever.

I often wondered why it was only the women who were to express publicly the grief. Why not the men?

My mother's brother died and before the year was up her father died, so she wore black clothing for a very long time.

My father did not approve of the custom of observing *luto*. One day the itinerant peddlers came by our place, selling shoes and clothing. My father bought a bright red Japanese kimono and gave it to my mother, saying, "It makes me so sad to see you wearing black all the time. Take that thing off and get into something bright." She put on the kimono and they smiled at each other. She never wore black clothing again, as far as I remember.

Years later my husband and I traveled to Spain and were pleasantly surprised to find so many similarities between Spain and New Mexico. The landscape is very similar — wide-open spaces, semi-arid deserts, plains and *meseta* [their word for *mesa*], with rugged mountains very much like ours.

It was great to hear our language spoken everywhere, which we seldom heard here. The foods in Spain were different — they don't have chile! — but other customs were very similar. We don't have the siesta down pat, as they did over there then, but we have often wished we did. Feast days are similar because of Catholicism in both countries. On one occasion we walked a long distance searching for a bookstore, and when we found it, it was closed, because of some saint's day. The same thing happened many times over, for one saint or another.

Women dressed in black were everywhere. They still observed *luto,* whereas by then it had died out for the most part in New Mexico. In fact the men were in on it over there — they had a black armband sewed to the left upper arm of their coats and shirts.

On the train from Madrid to Gijón we shared the compartment with a remarkable couple. She was a beautiful Spanish lady in her mid-forties. He was a very homely man in his eighties. He was big and fat for a man his age, and careless about his appearance, which accounted for the open fly. We thought they were father and daughter, but soon learned they were husband and wife.

His conversation revealed a proud and arrogant personality. When he learned that we were Americans, he made a big joke of how much money he was losing every day, because of the "Watergate" fiasco, which

was affecting economics all over the world. He told us
he had lost a huge fortune in the Cuban Revolution,
laughing all the while.

I wanted to talk to Liliana alone, but he dominated
the conversation, not allowing her a word in edgewise.
Luckily Don Fernando had to find a bathroom, and
while he was gone, she told her story hurriedly.

"When I was a very young girl, he wanted to marry
me, but I had a sick mother and could not leave her.
He was a very wealthy man, the type whom most of us
girls at that time wanted to marry, no matter how old
they were. We were thinking of security for our old
age, not wanting to become beggars. He had traveled
the world over, investing his money, and every time he
came back to Spain, he checked to see if I was ready
to be his wife. Each time the answer was, 'Not yet.'

"A couple of years ago my mother died and we
were married. I became the bird in a gilded cage. My
life became a fairy tale, hard to believe. The following
song is the story of my life:

     'Estaba la calandria
     Sentada en su balcón;
     En una jaula de oro
     Lloraba su prisión.'

"I have everything money can buy, except freedom.
Francisco lets me go to church, but I have to be home
ten minutes after mass is over, the time it takes me to
walk from the church to the house. If I am late,
because the mass is long, La Guardia Civil comes after
me, and without allowing an explanation he gives me
a scolding." She saw him coming down the aisle of the

train, and all conversation ceased.

As we got off the train, we found ourselves referring to them as "Beauty and the Beast." Nevertheless we were surprised when he invited us to visit them, before we left Gijón.

We learned later that many people in the town spoke angrily of Don Fernando. He was part of the Franco regime, and was directly responsible for the execution of many prominent citizens, who were friends and family of the people we met. We thought of him as an unusually cosmopolitan man. He had a certain sophistication which set him apart from other Spaniards we met in that area. Yet we sensed that his life was full of secrets.

Before we left we called on them to say goodbye. We were surprised to find where and how they lived. It was the penthouse of a large hotel, with *La Guardia Civil* standing guard, from the first floor to their very door at the top. It was a little frightening to see their lives, or rather his life, threatened to such an extent that all this security was necessary. But Fascist Spain was a strange place at that time.

Their home was filled with art and art objects from all over the world. A Chinese vase stood in the entryway. A Goya hung on the wall, next to a Velázquez, over a water fountain. He fondled some of the pieces on the sideboard in the dining room, telling us where they came from and how he had acquired them. Often he told us how much he had paid for each item.

We sat at a long dining room table, way too large for two people. Dignitaries may have come there, to plan their war strategies. I don't remember any other room in particular, but everything looked rich, polished and beautiful. Liliana looked sad, hardly speaking, doing only what he told her to do. She served us a glass of wine, and all I could think of was how sad she looked.

Don Fernando announced that he needed to shave. He left the room, but continued talking loudly, leaving the bathroom door open. We assumed it was to keep us from talking privately to Liliana.

After we returned to our humble little home, we often thought of Don Fernando and Liliana. We did not envy their opulent wealth. It was a great contrast to our home and the home I grew up in. My mother worked very hard all her life, but she had something Liliana lacked. I remember that shared smile, on the day of the red kimono, and I smile, too. Poor Liliana, in her cage of gold!

# # #

Lazy Mexicans

Tom came to New Mexico from "back east" after his stint in the armed services. He went to law school and became an attorney, specializing in bankruptcy. He studied photography under Ansel Adams and became a very good photographer. He loved woodworking and made many beautiful pieces of furniture out of Honduran mahogany.

He was an avid reader and loved the Spanish language. He took Spanish classes at the University of New Mexico until he became bilingual. He spent a long time in Mexico doing his art and learning about the country and its people. He also spent time in Spain, learning its language and literature. He was convinced that learning the second language made him a more aware and sensitive person.

Tom lived in a quiet neighborhood and enjoyed his neighbors. He was a curious man, who sometimes asked more questions than the neighbors wanted to discuss. One thing bothered him and that was why so many of them, especially Patricia, were so antagonistic against the people coming in from Mexico. Patricia did not speak Spanish, even though it was her parents' language. She went by the name of Patsy.

Tom disliked the name Patsy because of its other meanings, and always called her Patricia, pronouncing it in Spanish. She in turn called him Tom even though he preferred to be called Tomás, and most of his friends and neighbors did call him that.

Today was one of those times when he felt inquisitive and knew that if Patricia came over he would just have to ask her some questions. They had bothered him for a long time and maybe there were some which she had never faced.

He had written a history of Nicaragua and wanted to enlighten Patricia by giving her a copy and having her read it. She was now retired from teaching in the Public School system and had time on her hands. Tom wanted her to learn the history of Central America and of the United States' involvement in it. She listened or pretended to listen for a short while, but did not pick up the manuscript. Soon she resumed her recriminations against all Latinos, except those born in the United States.

"Perhaps you were lucky to have been born this side of the border," Tomás said to her, "for, you know, sooner or later they will come across that border in huge numbers and take back that which once belonged to them."

Patricia was furious! "Tom, you know that's not true; they're foreigners as far as I'm concerned, and they should not be permitted to come into our country."

There was silence for a few minutes. Tomás was waiting for her anger and indignation to die down a bit. He did not have a chance to continue because she stood up and left, saying, "I'll see you later, Tom."

Tomás did not see Patricia for a few days and felt sad about it. He was sorry he had angered her, but he couldn't help but wonder about many things. Why were people so unaware of what was happening in Central America, and in the world at large? He knew that most people depended on the daily paper or television, and that neither provided the truth about things. The mainstream press could not be trusted; they consistently misinformed the citizens, telling what the State Department or War Department or giant corporations wanted told.

A person couldn't possibly gain the truth about anything from 30-second sound bites. No story was ever told completely; the historical background was ignored. A person had to go beyond the media to see what the government was really up to. Tom knew that foreign news sources, like newspapers from Mexico or Spain, were more likely to see and tell it as it was.

Tomás was sitting on the back porch reading *The Nation,* when Patricia called to see if he needed anything from the grocery store. They were used to helping each other in this way, so he ordered a loaf of wheat bread and a quart of milk.

It was late evening when she came to bring the food, and he brought out a glass of wine for each. She was in a good mood, and so after a while Tomás brought out a second glass of wine. Soon she was telling him her adventures and frustrations of the day. The grocery store was way too big, she thought, and it was difficult finding what you wanted or anyone to help you. "Too many Mexicans speaking Spanish. You hear their language everywhere. They should speak English or go back to Mexico," she said. She raved on and on about how lazy they were and how useless. Tomás listened.

Quietly he said, "Wouldn't you like to learn to speak Spanish? After all, it's your language, and it's a beautiful language."

"No, I don't want to learn Spanish. I'm an American and here we speak English only," she answered angrily.

"You know, Patricia, you keep telling me that Mexicans are lazy, yet I notice that they work harder than anyone I know around here. The men do work which I consider the hardest of all the work in the world — roofing houses. Sometimes without modern equipment, they go up and down the ladder, in scorching weather, carrying buckets of hot tar for hours on end. The women clean the houses of the rich and take care of their children, having to neglect their own to do so. You've even said that they take away jobs from workers here, but really, they do jobs that no one else will do." Patricia sat quietly, looking out toward the mountains, not saying a word.

Tom continued. "The other day I heard someone praising a Mexican family. Each of the five works day and night, toiling to keep a roof over their heads, and to buy food. They do nothing but work, and they work all the time. They certainly are not lazy."

Patricia became very thoughtful, and Tom continued. "There has to be more to life than the hard struggle for daily bread. Is that all this land of milk and honey has to offer? They enjoy no week-ends, no vacations. There is literally no let-up from work. Would you like to live like that, Patricia?"

"No, that doesn't sound like fun," she said.

Both of them sat quietly, looking toward the mountains. "You know, Tom, you are making me rethink many things. We are so brain-washed in this society that it is difficult to think clearly. We Americans have been taught that we are so much better and so much smarter than anyone else on earth, so we believe that everybody else is inferior. It seems the more we have, the more we want others not to have, as if there wasn't enough. And all our defenses seem to be based on ignorance."

"How would you feel if you had to leave everything you had, everything familiar, and go to another country, just because inflation took all your savings, all your possessions, leaving you absolutely penniless?" Tom asked. "And then when you get here, wouldn't you hate to be treated the way we treat them?"

Patricia got up to leave and said, "Tomás, because I was a teacher all those years, I thought I knew everything. Now I realize that I have missed learning about the most important things — myself, other people and our backgrounds. I'll have to find my roots and learn to accept who I am, so that I can accept others the way they are."

She smiled and held out her hand. He took it and held it for a minute. She said, "Thank you, Tomás!"

# # #

An Empty Life

At the end of the month Dora was going to leave this hospital and, she hoped, never return. "What will you do with all that time on your hands?" asked the head nurse.

"Oh, I will sleep late every day, watch television, and keep my house nice and clean."

"Isn't that what you have done all along?"

"Well, not really. I always worried about getting to work on time. I've hated the routine of doing the same thing every day here and having to do all my chores on the week-end. By the time I've done that, I'm tired, and it's time to come back to work. For me, there will be no more sick people to take care of."

"Have you ever done any gardening?"

"No, the farming was always done by the men, and the women took care of the house and prepared the meals."

"You could take up some hobbies, maybe something you have always wanted to do just for fun, or learn something new."

"No, I'm old and too lazy to start now. I will enjoy just being at home."

The head nurse walked away, wondering why Dora had chosen a career she disliked so much. And she had to note that Dora was not good at it, because she didn't really like people.

Dora seldom spoke to anyone about her family. Her parents died long ago. Her husband had been dead several years. A daughter, who used to live with her, had also died recently, so only her married son was left. Dora lived alone and wondered what to do with her life now.

After a year of retirement she found it rather boring to sit around and do nothing but watch television. She had never acquired the love of reading, crocheting, knitting or any other kind of hand work which most women do. The days grew long and she realized that the people she knew during her working years, were either dead or had a busy life of their own. During her years as a nurse she had been completely unaware that life was changing and passing her by. She grew older and more and more detached from the outside world.

She had lived in the ancestral home all her life. After her parents died, she simply remained there. It was a comfortable house with familiar things all around. Her children were born there and there she had become a widow. The house and property were paid for and she had little to worry about, except that she was a very lonely person.

Her son had married a very ambitious woman who had no use for Dora, and there was no love lost between them. The daughter-in-law coveted the land and the house in which Dora lived.

Often, in the last few years the son told Dora that he

wanted to sell the house and property and promised to provide a smaller place for her. She dreaded leaving the familiar acreage and her large spacious home, for some unknown neighborhood where the houses all looked the same and were bunched together side by side like sardines.

Another element came to play in the equation. The city had built a community center next to her land and was very interested in buying the land in order to expand the center. The son heard about it, and immediately started pressuring her to sell. First he had to convince her that he knew how these matters worked and that he would take care of everything, if she would just transfer the property into his name. She had never thought that he was capable of understanding such matters, and mistrusted him completely.

This harassing went on for a couple of years, until she became sickly and in more need of her son's help. She had recently had eye surgery and every time he took her to the doctor or hospital, he reminded her that she could no longer take care of herself. He said this so many times that finally she began to believe him and realized she had to learn to trust him.

She had no one else to turn to. Her son seemed more attentive toward her lately than he had ever been in all his adult life. He had seldom visited her before, but now there was not a day when he did not call or stop by after work. Every time he visited, he brought up the necessity of selling the property, while it was still in demand.

Time went by and he finally convinced her to turn

over to him not only the house but also her personal checking account, claiming that her eyesight was so bad, that she could no longer write checks. All this happened so fast, that almost before she knew it, she was sick, weary and penniless. Now the son could do as he wished and she had little or nothing to say about anything. His wife was extremely happy that her husband had been clever enough to outsmart the old lady.

Dora could see it coming. The son sold everything she had and bought a small house on the outskirts of the city and moved her into it. The house was bought with her money, but legally the house belonged to him and his wife. Dora was to pay him three hundred dollars a month out of her social security check. He would deposit this money in his account, and that would help with the house payment and buy her a few groceries, providing she bought only necessities. Life had ceased to be worth living. She lived from hand to mouth, and all she wanted to do was die.

She began to wonder why she should continue taking her medication, when it didn't make her feel any better. One day she emptied the pills from all three bottles into one and shook them well. She admired the beautiful colors — blue, green and yellow — and then decided not to take them any more. After a few days she was feeling better, not worse! The doctor assumed that the medication was doing her good, and was very pleased with her progress. But the lack of medication was really having the exact opposite effect from what Dora wanted.

When Dora grasped this, she reversed the process, and took double the number of pills prescribed. She became sluggish and disinterested in life. She began to realize that the process of death was too slow, just as that of birth sometimes was. The only difference was that her birth had been someone else's responsibility, and her death was hers alone.

On the day her son was to take her for her check-up and a new prescription she became very anxious. She managed to get a pitcher of water, a glass and the bottle of pills to the kitchen table. She sat there and swallowed one by one, one pill after another, alternating colors, first a green, then a blue, then a yellow, and then another round, until they were all gone. As she swallowed the last one, she smiled to herself and said, "That was fun!" She went to bed and made herself comfortable. Blotto.

The son found her there and could not suppress a smile.

Later the police found a note, which said, "My son's constant nagging forced me to do this."

# # #

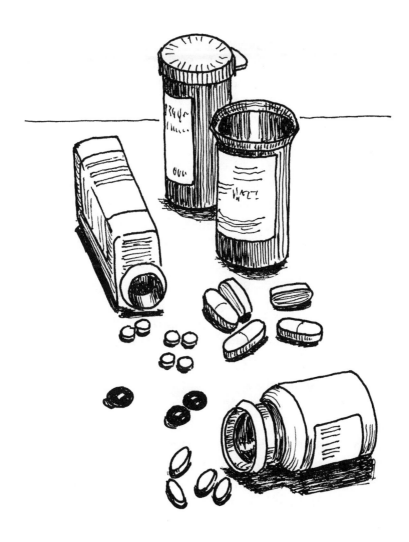

Before Columbus

When Tom moved to New Mexico from "back east," he fell in love with the wide open spaces, the sunshine, the people and their language. He took day trips on week-ends all over the state. He loved the mountains and the desert, and often said, "The only thing New Mexico lacks is an ocean."

He became interested in the cultures that were already here before the Europeans arrived. He discovered that the state was full of archaeological sites and became more deliberate in his exploring. First he went to Quarai and Gran Quivira in the mountains east of Albuquerque. At Bandelier Monument near Los Alamos he climbed up the hill and up the ladder to the kiva. The cliff dwellings fascinated him. The Puyé ruins near Santa Clara Pueblo were another interesting site, very similar to Bandelier. He wondered why talented people built in such precarious places, and why they later left.

At the Aztec State Monument near Farmington, he loved the size and grandeur of the Great Kiva. He sat in the center of the open space and meditated while native drums throbbed. From there he crossed the state line into Colorado, in order to explore Mesa Verde.

The cliff dwellings there were much more extensive, indicating the presence of a complex society. The history of the people who had inhabited the area was of great interest to him. Where had they come from? And again Tom wondered why they built the way they did, requiring someone to descend hundreds of feet on ladders or handholds in the rock, to bring water to the village in pots. They also had to climb up to the top over the edge of the cliff to work their fields of corn and beans. Why did they make life so hard? And again, whey did they leave? What happened to them?

As spring break approached, Tom heard some of the younger students at the U. planning a trip to Yucatán, to see the pyramids there. He read up on Mayan archaeological ruins, and didn't hesitate to schedule a flight to Cancún.

He found it to be a most unusual city, which didn't exist twenty-five years ago. The site was selected — reportedly by computer — by a consulting firm for the Department of Tourism of the Mexican government. They were looking for a development site that would boost Yucatán's primitive economy. Since then an old fishing village had been transformed into an international tourist resort.

There was a huge Hotel Zone, on an island shaped like the numeral seven, at the northeast corner of the peninsula. Every American hotel chain was represented, providing 25,000 rooms. Inland, across the lagoon, was downtown Cancún, a booming city of more than 300,000 people.

Tom stayed in the city, not the Hotel Zone. He talked to the waiters and working people there, asking them if they liked living and working in Cancún. They answered, "No," every time.

"Why not?" he asked.

"No hay tradición aquí." [There is no tradition here.] They told him they went back to their native villages, during vacations and holidays, to keep contact with tradition. It was somehow sad, Tom thought, that something so important was missing in the midst of this thriving tourism industry, built up so suddenly. Twenty-five years is not enough history to provide what these people knew they needed.

The Mayan people have been in Yucatán for several thousand years, but their history has to be unearthed from the archaeological ruins which cover the area. More than 1200 sites have been noted, and the area is a dream come true for anyone interested in archaeology.

Tom knew he could not possibly see all the sites, but he knew he had to visit the most important ones during the short time he had in Yucatán. He rented a VW bug, for surprisingly little, and headed south toward Tulum. The beautiful, clear blue water of the Caribbean fulfilled his deepest longings for ocean and surf. The water beckoned to him to come in and romp. Tulum is a beautiful village, the only major Mayan ruin with a beach. Iguanas climbed on the broken walls, and basked in the sun. Tom was totally enchanted with Tulum.

He drove forty miles in an absolutely straight line into the interior. The two-lane paved highway was a green corridor through the jungle. At times he passed native Mayan huts — no running water, no electricity

— a complete contrast to the modern city of Cancún. Stolid faces stared at him, as he sped by.

His arrival at Cobá was sudden. He found a dirt parking lot, a tiny stand where he could buy a soft drink, and then a mile-long hike on a path through the *selva.* He came to an area of broken columns, and could see unexcavated mounds of rock covered with vegetation. The highest one, the pyramid, had been only partly uncovered by archaeologists. He clambered up it, feeling good, pleased that he had the chance to be there before the scientists put everything in its proper place. At the top was the typical sacrificial room, extending up above the jungle canopy. From there he could look for miles out over the treetops. It felt to him that time stood still.

Back in Cancún, Tom knew he still had to visit the really big site, at Chichén Itzá. Cancún was plagued with people selling time-share condos and special guided tour tickets. One of them told him that the Spring Equinox was going to provide something special at Chichén Itzá, so he joined a bus tour that was going on that day. The busses arrived around noon, just in time for a splendid meal at the hotel/restaurant.

He joined the people walking amid the multi-colored bougainvillea on the path to the plaza of the ruins. The main pyramid was huge and completely restored by the archaeologists. He climbed to the top, with others. From there he could see many other wonders. Tom realized that the Europeans were not the only ones with advanced architectural talent. That particular science was well-developed before

Europeans arrived.

One area had been the marketplace, with many stalls, huge columns in rows, looking almost Greek in style, with a wide stairway up to the special shrine room on top. He could see the ball field in the distance, and beyond it was "the observatory," where the Mayans studied the stars. Further over under the trees, he could see a small body of water. Other visitors told him it was the *"estanque,"* the well of human sacrifice.

A large number of people was gathering in the open space near the foot of the main pyramid. Several thousand people, students and tourists from all over the world, sat on the ground and waited patiently. A woman with dark skin and a brilliant smile invited Tom to sit with her on her blanket. Tom's interest in what was happening helped him overcome his shyness, and he sat. "What's going on?" he asked.

"We're waiting for the serpent to descend," she said.

"Serpent?" Tom asked.

"The plumed serpent. The one the Aztecs called Quetzalcoatl. The Maya have another older name for him."

"Descend?"

"As the sun sets on the equinox, which is today, a shadow will come down the edge of the pyramid, giving us the illusion of the plumed serpent, creeping down from heaven to earth. As the sun lowers itself little by little, the shadows will look like the serpent descending."

"So the builders here knew what they were doing when they located that huge pyramid where they did," Tom said.

The woman's smile was mysterious, Tom thought. The crowd waited patiently. The children were not running and screaming. People sat, talked quietly, and waited.

But on that particular day, just as it was to happen, a cloud covered the face of the sun, and the shadow did not appear. The crowd accepted the disappointment with remarkable calm. Tom knew he would have to return to Yucatán some day, to see that shadow, to experience the myth of the descent of the Plumed Serpent.

# # #

Magic Interlude

When I was a young girl, Vallecitos was a magical town, nestled in a valley between hills and mountains, with a stream flowing down its middle. There was a Catholic Church, a grade school, a dance hall, a United Brethren Mission, and the Amador Mercantile Company and Post Office. The CCC camp was a later addition to the town.

As time went by the young people left for better economic opportunities, and the old gradually passed away. Only a very few of the natives have remained. Some outsiders have come to establish themselves in this lovely valley, but on a recent visit my impression was that it was almost a ghost town compared to what it had been.

My Uncle Alberto owned the Amador Mercantile Company, which provided the necessities of life for the town, including food, clothing and farm machinery. Whatever the townspeople needed he ordered for them and had it shipped to the wholesale house in San Juan Pueblo, where he picked it up each week.

He also had several thousand head of sheep. When they were sheared, the wool was also taken to the wholesalers, from where it was shipped out. The sheepherders came down from the mountains each week with loads of firewood, which Uncle Albert also sold. His work force all came from the town or nearby villages. His business had been there for decades and lasted for over fifty years.

Los Amadores had a beautiful old house, attached to the store, with large rooms and 15-foot high ceilings. The house was very cool in the summer, but hard to heat in the winter. The front door to the living room was beautifully carved and had an unusual doorbell. There was no button to push — a visitor turned a key a time or two, to make the bell ring inside the house.

A large L-shaped porch looked out over the lawn and flower garden. Many hours were spent on the porch swing. Not only family members enjoyed this place, but also customers waiting for someone to open the mercantile after ringing the doorbell. This became customary, when Uncle Albert was not tending the store, and especially after the folks got older.

The interior walls of the house were painted white, but everything else was royal blue. Not only the woodwork, but also the kitchen range, was royal blue. That was my Aunt Florentina's favorite color.

The kitchen had a large bay window with a wide seat with cushions, where my cousin Anita and I sat or lay down in the evening and watched the moon come over the mountain. That was our favorite song.

"When the moon comes over the mountain,
That's the day that I'll come home to you."
We were teen-agers and could only see things from a romantic point of view. We loved to dance. The dance hall was just across the road from the store, so they let

us go, as long as we were home before midnight.

The bay window was our hang-out. The few winter days I visited them, Anita and I enjoyed the warmth of the sun there. We shared our secret thoughts and dreams, about boys. My uncle and aunt were much more open about those kinds of discussions than were my parents, and they only smiled when they overheard our whispering and laughter.

In the early 30's my Uncle Alberto bought a piano and had it shipped to Vallecitos. It came by horse and wagon over incredibly rutted dirt roads. The piano was for Anita, their only daughter. She was quite talented and soon played it very well, by ear. Later she took lessons from one of the missionaries, and still later received music training at the University of New Mexico.

My uncle played the guitar, and evenings after dinner were usually spent making music. I remember him getting up from the dinner table, saying, "C'mon, let's make music!" Old songs, including, *"La Barca de Oro," "El Rancho Grande,"* and *"Cielito Lindo"* reso-nated through the house and filled one's heart with joy.

Anita and I spent much time together, in winter at boarding school in Santa Cruz, and once in a while I visited her and her family for a day or two after the school term ended in the summer, or before it started in the fall. We hiked the hills alone, or with her family.

Tía Florentina had a way of making us look at things: the wild flowers, the birds, and even the pebbles at our feet. I remember how she explained that the stones would look different once we took them away from their original place. She insisted that we learn to pay attention to natural things. Often after a hike we came down to the creek to cool our hot and weary feet in the cold water. That was a magical place and certainly a magical time in our lives!

This family was very good for me! I came from a large family, with a very strict upbringing. The work ethic was firmly imprinted in my brain — canning, cleaning, washing, ironing and cooking. Anita, in contrast, laughed, joked, played the piano and sang. That was her work!

I considered myself very lucky to share in the joy of this fun-loving family, if only for a few hours or days at a time. Magic! Her parents doted on her, and although Anita's wants were few, she got what she wanted. Her parents were successful in their business, and Anita didn't have to worry about money, and didn't really think about that at all.

Her two older brothers, Alberto and Leopoldo, had gone away to college and come home to become teachers. Anita went to UNM for a couple of years, but wasn't much interested in a degree. She was there for fun, and often said, "I'm here, looking for a man!"

She married and had three children. Unfortunately she also developed multiple sclerosis, and died very young. My uncle spent all he had, trying to find a cure for Anita. They tried medical doctors in Española and Santa Fe. They tried native herb treatments of all kinds. They tried religious healers. Oral Roberts took a big chunk for every time he saw her. Besides the

trips to Oklahoma, he charged $300 for prayer and
laying on of hands. Anita died, and her parents were
impoverished before the end.

Life deals us a hand of cards, and what we're dealt
sometimes seems to determine more than how we play
the game. Here I am, half a century later, writing
about how much she enjoyed her short life. Hers was
over very early, and I'm still enjoying mine. Who said
life was fair?

#   #   #

Música

Marta and Elena had known each other since childhood, and now that their families were grown and gone, they enjoyed many things together.

They heard of an African/Cuban concert that was coming to town called *"Mezcla"* and bought tickets. They had been to Cuba together in one of the Venceremos Brigade Study/Work Tours, and had come to love the country, its people and especially the music.

Their anticipation grew as the evening of the concert approached. The theater was full. The hour arrived and everyone was quiet, but there seemed to be some kind of delay. They knew that most Latin programs never started on time, so they were not surprised. Finally the performers appeared and the program began without checking the audio system. When the music began, there were squeaks and scratches, and Marta and Elena wondered how long it would take them to correct it.

There were drums, cymbals, a saxophone, several electrical guitars, a keyboard and other percussion instruments. The master of ceremonies described each song in Spanish. They were about the revolution, the US embargo, and how the people of Cuba had coped during all those years. He played the mandolin and sang, but the percussion was so loud that it drowned every word. The evening became too long, and what they hoped would be music turned into noise.

On the way to the parking lot Marta asked, "Well, what did you think? Was it loud enough for you?"

They laughed, and Elena said, "It wasn't at all what I had expected. I was straining my ears to hear some popular song we learned when we were there not that long ago. Remember how they woke us every morning with, *¡Buenos Dias, América!*? I don't know why I expected them to do that one, but I did. When the singer started each song, I caught the first line, but the saxophone came in so loud that he blew the words right over our heads. That made me angry."

"I felt the same way," said Marta. "The amplifiers should be thrown out. I can understand using them, when the concert is held outdoors or in a very large auditorium, and even then they could tone it down. Anyway, it seems that the masses are there for the noise and confusion only; words don't seem to matter much any more."

"Don't say that," Elena laughed. "If they hear us, they'll say we're too old to appreciate their music."

"What music?" Marta asked. "There was a time when a song had meaningful words, easy to remember. The tune stuck in your mind and you hummed it through the day with a smile on your face. Now we go to a concert, expecting to hear at least one familiar tune, but go home disappointed. As far as I'm concerned, amplifiers are one of the worst inventions!"

"Is it because they have no respect for your

eardrums?" laughed Elena, making fun of Marta. "Maybe they think eardrums are replaceable!" They were tired and sleepy, and went straight home.

The following week they met and continued their conversation on music. By that time they had both done a lot of thinking about it.

"You know, Elena," Marta said, "All week I've been thinking of my mother and the songs she sang. She had a good voice and we loved to hear her sing and often sang along with her. Her favorite was *La Barca de Oro*. I can still hear her.

> *"Yo ya me voy Al puerto donde se halla*
> *La barca de oro Que ha de conducirme.*
> *Yo ya me voy, Solo vengo a despedirme.*
> *Adiós mujer, Adiós para siempre, adiós."*

Elena became animated. "Those were songs which told a story. He's leaving on a golden boat, and he's saying goodbye. That kind of song starts somewhere, then goes somewhere and says something. Even the funny, lively ones, like *La Cucaracha,* tell a story."

"It's true," Marta said.

Elena was remembering. "In school we sang patriotic songs like, *O Fair New Mexico* and *America the Beautiful.* In Sunday School we sang *Jesus Loves Me* and *Heavenly Sunshine.*"

Marta made a funny face at the mention of Sunday School. But the topic of music had her excited. "With the radio we were in touch with the Big Band Era.

Remember how we loved *Chattanooga Choo-Choo, In the Mood, South of the Border, Stormy Weather, Blue Skies, Star Dust* and many others.

"Glee Club was my favorite," said Elena. The teachers seemed almost afraid of our Mexican zing and salsa, afraid of the suggestion of 'romance,' or whatever. Maybe it was our hormones they were afraid of — and we didn't even know the word! But the songs they taught us had plenty of whatever it was that scared them, it seems to me! *Love's Old Sweet Song* and *Flow Gently, Sweet Afton.* They were bringing us their version of the same basic love stories. Even *Comin' through the Rye.*

> 'Every lassie hae her laddie,
> Nane, they say, hae I.
> Yet all the boys, they smile at me,
> While comin' through the rye.'

"That *is* a song of romance, no matter what language it came from. Everybody has hormones!" Marta laughed.

Elena interrupted. "Remember in boarding school, how we mangled the hymns, to make them funny! They added some fun to our lives, even when we were later punished. I'll never forget the look on Miss Bower's face, when she heard us singing our version of, *At the Cross.* We changed it a bit, remember?

> "At the bar, at the bar,
> Where I smoked my first cigar,

And my nickels and my dimes rolled away —
It was there by chance
That I tore my Sunday pants,
And now I have to wear them every day!"

Marta had joined in the singing, and they were laughing so hard, they sounded like teen-agers and were glad no one else could hear them.

Marta said, "You know, we were pretty terrible. I recall another one:

"How dry I am! How dry I am!
Nobody seems to give a damn..."

They sat and talked for a long time. Elena had seen a television program, where a music professor at NYU was teaching old songs in a community center. The professor said, "Children can't carry a tune these days, because they never heard one. They think that singing is nothing but words and rhythm."

"You mean like rap?" said Marta. "I've been listening to some of it, and trying to understand it. There is so much self-loathing in the lyrics. All I hear is that everything is a fraud and nothing turns out right. The list of things they don't do well goes on forever. They don't do relationships. They have no talent and are incapable of selfless love."

"They don't sound like the kind of songs I want to learn and sing for enjoyment," said Elena.

"Neither do I," agreed Marta. "Maybe that kind of music's too real." They both laughed.

"We can always look forward to the Reversal of the Tao," Elena suggested. "What goes up, must come down. The pendulum swings to the right, and then to the left. The cycle of the seasons goes round and round. The spring of hope is forever. Music changes with the times, and with each generation. I'm glad we can still remember what you and I think of as 'the good music.' Maybe it will come back. Yet it's hardly fair either that we impose what we liked on the young!"

# # #

Cavemen

Tom was certainly no spelunker. He had a slight
case of claustrophobia, inherited from his mother. He
seemed especially sensitive to "bad air," and felt just
a little nervous in places that were too closed-in. The
story of Tom Sawyer and Becky Thatcher lost in a
cave terrified him, when he first read it as a boy.

An experience in Mitla, a Zapotec ruin in Oaxaca,
didn't help much. The tour guide showed them all
around the marvelous temple. Tom was amazed that
what looked like a mosaic on a wall was really the tip-
ends of delicate stone pieces more than a foot long,
fitted into place with an amazing exactitude. They were
not pieces glued onto a wall — they were the wall
itself.

The guide took them into *"la tumba,"* appropriately
named, Tom thought. Just as they arrived down in the
dark closed space, which supposedly contained tombs,
the guide lit a cigarette. Tom was stunned. "Here we
are," he thought, "twenty people, more than that, with
a limited supply of oxygen molecules to take care of
all of us, and he sets fire to them!" Tom dallied for a
little longer, but found he could no longer pay attention
to what the guide was saying. He turned away, dashed
back up the narrow passage they had come down, and
stumbled, bumping his head badly. He staggered out

into the sun and air, very glad to be out of there.

Back home in New Mexico, however, Tom found he couldn't omit a visit to Carlsbad Caverns. It was an internationally famous attraction and widely regarded as one of the natural wonders of the world. It had been discovered less than a hundred years ago, and the only known incidence of human habitation in the cave was a brief episode of mining bat guano, before it was made into a National Park. Tom's inquiries and investigations assured him that ventilation would not be a serious problem, when he visited.

He drove to Carlsbad and joined the group of tourists who visited the cave. They walked down a paved and lighted path. The place was huge, with stairways and handholds and railings, and rangers. The natural formations were nothing short of marvelous. Tom was especially impressed with what was called The Big Room, a very large open area a thousand or more feet underground, with a paved dry path which went all around it. It hardly felt like a cave at all.

And The Lunch Room seemed almost out of place — a large open area, not far from the Big Room, brilliantly lighted, with tables and benches and lunch for sale. A fast modern elevator took tourists back to the surface. Persons were discouraged from trying to climb out on foot.

Tom's study of pre-Columbian cultures led him to a site very near to his home in Albuquerque. Sandia Man Cave in the Sandia Mountains provided very important evidence as to how long humanity has been in the area, much longer than previously supposed.

When Tom visited the cave, he found there really wasn't much to see. Charred spots were on the wall and ceiling of a shallow opening in the rock, very high above Las Huertas Creek. Bones and stone tools and artifacts of hide and woven yucca had been removed by the archaeologists.

Claustrophobia never entered Tom's mind. It was the time involved that impressed him. Perhaps as much as 20,000 years ago, Siberians came across and moved south all those thousands of miles from the Bering Sea. Julius Caesar was 2000 years ago. Abraham was 4000 years ago. The invention of agriculture as less than 10,000 years ago. This was more than twice as long ago.

Tom's reading about ancient cultures led him to a study of world mythology, especially the writings of Joseph Campbell. In a book called, *PRIMITIVE MYTHOLOGY,* Campbell described the cave art of Southern France and Northern Spain. These people were hunters as well as artists, and their paintings on cave walls were part of their magic, seeking to assure successful hunting.

Tom was interested, but put it aside in his mind, and went on with his life. His ongoing study of the Spanish language at the University led him to sign up for a summer in Gijón, in Asturias on the northern coast of Spain. He signed up for two courses. One was *Cultura de España.* The other was *Cuentos Hispánicos.*

When the group assembled in Gijón, they learned that the culture course was to be taught by a native of Gijón, a cousin of a professor at the University of New

Mexico. The course on *cuentos* was to be taught by a native of New Mexico, a member of the Spanish Department at UNM.

Tom had already gone to work on the *cuentos* course, he thought. He found people in restaurants, hotels, and at the boardwalk, ready to talk about the Spanish Civil War, which had ended almost thirty years earlier. Franco had not yet died, but many conversations contained the phrase, *"cuando muera Franco."* The Spanish professor even told a joke to his class, on the first day. Two *españoles* were visiting Moscow. They joined the line which passed in front of Lenin's Tomb. One said to the other, as they stared at the embalmed body of the former leader, *"Oh, sí — eso tenemos en casa."* [oh, yes — we have that at home.]

Tom was sure the class could collect a book — *CUENTOS DE LA GUERRA CIVIL.* When the *cuentos* class met, the professor pulled out a manila folder, opened it and announced, "The complete title of this course is, *Cuentos Hispánicos de Nuevo Méjico,* and proceeded for the rest of the summer, as if the class were located in New Mexico, not in Spain.

The school was frustrating for Tom. It was mostly a lark in a foreign country, for students and professors, not a serious inquiry into anything. He remembered his reading about the Caves of Altamira, located not far from Gijón. He asked the professors about them. The Spanish professor suggested a class tour by bus, and it was arranged.

Tom was in a strange state of mind as the group

toured the cave. He felt something like awe. The paintings were remarkable — extremely life-like, almost as if they could breathe and move — bison, reindeer, horses, oryx, mammoths. Tom forgot his claustrophobia, even though the space was tight in places.

There was some electric light provided, but it was minimal. Tom wondered how the original painters could do such marvelous work, by torchlight. Surely they couldn't do it in the absolute dark. At one point in the tour, the lights were turned off, so that the group could see just how dark it really was. It was total dark.

Back on the bus, Tom was in a sort of daze. Thirty thousand years! Not three thousand, which goes back to King Solomon — no, thirty thousand. Tom was brought back to reality, when the *cuentos* professor stated, "Well, it doesn't compare to Carlsbad Caverns!"

Tom was speechless. He wanted to say that it didn't compare to the Empire State Building either, but he held his peace. He didn't want to argue. He wanted to stay in the trance-like state of mind he was still in, caused by the very idea of thirty thousand years.

# # #

Progress

Now that I am an old man, I feel like a survivor of a terrible storm. It's not easy confronting the dark side of our New Mexico history. There are too many unpleasant truths about our past.

Before the Civil Rights Act was passed, and enforced, there was horrific discrimination against the Mexican people here in our state. We were not Hispanics or Spanish then; we called ourselves *"Mejicanos."* It was a good name, for it meant *mestizos,* a combination of Spanish, Native American and Mexican blood.

In some towns we found signs in restaurants and swimming pools which read, "No Mexicans or Dogs Allowed."

I worked throughout the state in whatever job I could find in order to furnish a living for my family — a carpenter by trade, but a jack of all trades, for bread. I put up and repaired windmills, often spending all day in the hot sun, but was forced to look forward to a lonely night under the stars in the back of my pick-up. For dinner I ate whatever was left in my lunch pail. There was literally no other place for me to lay my head — no motel, no hot meal in a restaurant. Mexicans were forced to carry their food and bedding, no matter how far we had to go from home, to do

118

whatever work we could find.

I remember even in the late 50's it was very difficult getting a motel for the night. One time I took my two boys on a fishing trip, hoping to stay overnight in a certain town I won't name. We passed several motels and finally found one which had a sign out — "Vacancy." When the proprietor saw the little brown faces of my boys, he told me there was no vacancy.

I said, "Your sign out there says, 'Vacancy.'"

"It has just been taken," he said. Then he added, "We do have a vacant cabin out back. It has no running water, but there is an outhouse farther back."

We left. The boys were disappointed, and I'm sure they didn't quite understand all the undercurrents of the man's words and actions. I could tell that he was a blatant liar. I knew that I would never stop or even go through that town again as long as I lived. Maybe things have changed, but sometimes it seems they haven't really, very much. From inside their domain, the ruling group can always lie to us. I know mine was not an isolated case.

In the motels, Mexicans did all the dirty work, as they do today, but we were not allowed to enjoy a hot bath and a bed. In the restaurants they did the cooking, the dish-washing and the cleaning, but were not allowed to eat a meal.

This discrimination was not only against Mexicans. Blacks and Native Americans were not allowed to enter the inner-sanctum either. One of my daughters had a black friend named Diana. The families enjoyed picnics together and often ate at each other's homes.

My daughter suggested going out to eat sometime, and Diana said, "Great! We can go to Furr's Cafeteria!"

My daughter wondered why Furr's.

"That's the only eating place where we feel comfortable," Diana said. "They have opened their doors to everyone and are smart enough to know that money is money and has the same value coming from either a white or a black hand." That happened some time before the Civil Right Act was passed.

Right after the Civil Rights Act, places of business were made to post a sign saying, "This establishment does not discriminate against anyone." They were afraid to be shut down, but continued to get around it using the "No Vacancy" sign.

A lawyer neighbor once told me, "Laws were made to be broken. They not only break, but they bend. If a law was never made, it could not be broken." I did not understand exactly what he meant at the time, and always thought of him as a crooked lawyer. Experience has taught me more about the breaking and bending of laws — I'm convinced it happens daily.

The fact that we were not good enough to eat in restaurants or sleep in motels was not enough. We did all the hard work which no one else would do, and at the same time were called "lazy." I wonder if there's something wrong with the English language!

And speaking of language, efforts have been made to get rid of Spanish ever since I can remember. My children went to boarding school and were made to feel inferior because they used Spanish. Demerits were given to them every time a teacher heard them speak a word of Spanish. After so many marks they were given special work duties as punishment for having fallen from grace. They were made to scrub the floors and do hand laundry, for knowing and using their own language!

One daughter brought home poor grades in a class which was called, "Spanish." "What's that about?" I asked.

"I know more about it than she does, and she can't stand that," my daughter said. Then she added with a little grin, "And I guess I get impudent about it, sometimes." Imagine! My children, brown as they are among all those lily-white missionary teachers! The teachers' zeal made them view us as uncivilized heathen, unworthy of any natural human dignity. They came here to change us! Even our language was not allowed.

Now all these years later, after we thought linguists had proved that knowing two languages was always better than knowing only one, we have the same problem all over again. "English only!" is the refrain. Nearly always, two of anything is better than one — *¿Qué no?* Two languages give two points of view. You get to walk in the other fellow's moccasins, understanding him better and overcoming some of the tendency to discriminate against him.

They say it's better now than it was, and I guess it is, a little. Sometimes I think the basic problem is not much better. There are too many people who still think they're better than other people and they have a way of getting what they want.

The last time I was out, and I don't get out much any more, we went to a restaurant, and there it was — a sign at the cash register, "We reserve the right to refuse service to anyone." What does that really mean? What is going on? Has the Civil Rights Act been repealed, when I wasn't looking? Isn't that sign itself a violation of the law? It's pretty clear, to me. It means that we Mexicans may or may not qualify to go into those establishments and receive service. Some progress!

# # #

Chicanas on the Move

"It seems absurd that it often takes a war or some great catastrophic event to bring about change for the good in a society," Carmen said to Lupe. "Remember how it was in World War II, when our husbands went away to do their soldiering, and we were left alone to care for our families?"

"Yes, I do remember," said Lupe, "and life was never the same again. We were jerked out of a very conservative way of life, into being both father and mother to the kids. We had to pay the bills and make the decisions. Poor guys! They thought they'd come back to the same gals they left behind. It never occurred to them that we would change. Like I say, we were forced to make decisions for ourselves, and we made them, right or wrong. Often wrong, maybe! Ha!" They both laughed. "But when my husband came back, he intended to take over all that, and it didn't work. I had learned how to think for myself."

"The first time I had to pay the monthly bills, I didn't know where to start," said Carmen. "My husband was such a macho that he made the money and he was in charge of it. I used to have to ask him, if I needed a dollar, and he always knew what I bought with it. After he was gone, I was very careful with money. There was so little of it, because the soldiers'

pay was so small then. I figured out I had to go to
work to augment the family income."

"So did I," said Lupe. "Lucky for me I was a good
typist and soon found a job with Kelly Girls. I knew
all along what I wanted to do, which was go to the
University, but I got married instead, and had a baby.
After my husband went to war, my mother took care
of my little one, bless her, and I was on my way. I
enrolled at the U and began my juggling act. Early to
rise, take my little girl to Mother's, work eight hours
typing, take night courses. Staying busy made the days
and weeks go faster, and I didn't have time to be
lonely."

"Boy, my life wasn't that simple," said Lupe
laughing. "I couldn't get a job here in New Mexico,
because there weren't any. A friend of mine told me
that there were defense jobs in California, provided by
the war machine, and she was going there. We began
talking about it and decided that together we could
manage our three children and share expenses. Her
folks loaned her some money, but I had to wait for the
first of the month for the allotment check.

"We landed in Long Beach and soon went to work
for Douglas Aircraft, installing electrical wiring on
C-47's. They started us at a dollar-eight an hour for
swing shift, and we thought that was good. On
Saturdays it was time-and-a-half, $1.62 an hour. It
seems terrible now, such little pay, but it was great
then. The war was a long one, and my husband was
one of those who never came back. By then I was used
to managing alone."

"Our lives were similar in some ways," said Carmen. "My husband came back, but he wasn't the same man I had married. I, too, had changed. I was no longer willing to give up my hard-won freedom and go back to where we had been. You know, life goes on and changes take place, whether you're together or apart. He came back, thinking he could continue life where he had left off. Home from work, pick up a beer and sit in front of the radio until dinner time. And how about me? Home from work, pick up my daughter, prepare dinner, wash dishes, get clothes ready for all of us next day. No way.

"We were divorced shortly after he returned. By then I was teaching school, earning my own money. My daughter was seven years old, and we had grown accustomed to living alone. His absence had liberated me from that old repressed way of life, and I could never go back."

"I wonder whether it was religion, or our mothers, who taught us to 'love, honor and obey' our husbands," asked Lupe. "I can see that it's different for our daughters. It wasn't as easy for them to make the same mistakes we did. Religion was less powerful, and the girls were liberated sexually, which made everything different."

"You're right," said Carmen. "And our kids helped us understand some things. I remember when my son came home from University classes, and we talked and talked. He had become very proud of the fact that he was 'chicano.' I had never used the word. I had heard my family talk about it sometimes, in a most disparaging way. They seemed to hate the word, and wanted to call themselves 'Spanish.' But we aren't Spanish. I know, because I went there and checked that out. The Spaniards despise us."

"You felt that in Spain?" Lupe asked.

"Yes, they think we're simply 'Mexicans,' and look down their noses. I remember asking my son about what the word 'chicano' meant to him.

"He told me that we were not born in Spain, nor in Mexico, and were not Native Americans, and that the word refers to those of us who have been here over three hundred years, descendants from the mixture of all those people. They had found a word that described who they were without confusion.

"My son thinks the people who don't like the word are afraid of the political implications. When it came out into the media in the 60's, it was part of the protest against the Vietnam War, and then part of César Chavez' movement to obtain justice for the farm workers. I learned much from my son, and all my kids. They were certainly more free, at an earlier age, than we were."

"Yes," agreed Lupe. "Things have changed. We have changed!"

"It's true," said Carmen, "but I wonder about the long run. Sometimes I think things like this go in circles. Or maybe it's like a pendulum, swinging from one extreme to the other. We had the war and the liberation it brought. Our daughters had the 60's, and hippies, and Women's Lib. Then came the 80's, with one step forward and two steps back. Fundamentalism took hold, and it became more popular to be superficially 'religious' than openly liberated. The popular theme, just now, is that the wife should 'submit gracefully.' Such bullshit!"

"Yeah!" exclaimed Lupe. "Back to being barefoot and pregnant. The more kids you have, the more your imprisonment is assured. The birth-control pill was a pure blessing for those of us who had sense enough to use it. Popes and preachers who say it's a sin to use it are simply out of it! What's the matter with them? I guess they never heard about the population explosion and what ails our world. Mother Earth cannot possibly support our thoughtlessness and arrogance. I find myself admiring couples who have conscientiously decided that for them Zero Population is the answer."

"Well, you seem to see my point, that we're going in reverse just now," said Carmen. "I was standing in line at the grocery store the other day and the talk there scared me. So many women talk as if they thought of themselves as underlings of their husbands. He makes the decisions, tells them how life is, and they cower under his control and command."

"There is that," admitted Lupe. "But the cat is out of bag. You can even see it on the highway. A young chicana, in a fast car, changing lanes, on her way! And I imagine her poor macho husband, someone she wouldn't have to bother with at all, if she had not made a mistake as a teen-ager — sitting at home with his beer can in his hand, scowling at the TV set as it screams at him, wondering where she is, why she has to go to school, why she has a job and money of her

own, and what he can do about it! She's on her way
and mothers and grandmothers and Popes and
preachers are not going to stop her."

"'Hooray for her!' I say," cried Carmen, and the
two old women had a good laugh together.

# # #

More Memories, Dreams, Reflections

Teotihuacan
In Old Mexico — an archeological site — The
Pyramid of the Sun
The largest pre-Columbian city in this hemisphere
So high — at such an angle
I look up from its base and it intimidates me.
The stairs are not deep enough for one's feet.
No rope or railing is provided.
I came here now, so that I wouldn't be too old to
climb it.
Am I already too old to make it to the top?
I see an old woman coming down and I wait to talk
to her.
She tells me she is 84 years old and climbs the
pyramid once a year, every year.
I take heart and begin the climb.
It takes time to reach the top.
My husband and I sit in the lotus position.
We ask someone to take our picture.
We feel we are on top of the world,
looking down on the Pyramid of the Moon and the
Avenue of the Dead.
We hold hands and smile, and are speechless,
looking down on the remains of one of the greatest
human civilizations.

Thankful that we are here
Going back in time.

# # #

Life for a child seems to move very slowly. As I
look back on my life, there seem to be long periods in
which little happened. But the special times, the
exciting moments, stand out.

# # #

I remember being taken as a little girl, to "see the
Christmas lights" in Madrid, New Mexico, a coal-
mining town on the road between Tijeras Canyon and
Cerrillos. No one had yet explained to me about make-
believe, so I thought that everything I saw was real.
Such a wonderful world!

In Sunday School we had learned all about the
angels and the birth of Christ. We had sung the
Christmas songs with gusto. But what we learned was
something that had happened long ago and far away.
Now I could see it with my own eyes! I believed that
I was seeing real angels and Joseph and Mary.

Besides the manger-scene there was a train which
went around the town, piloted by Santa himself, who
gave rides and goodies to the children. There we found
the Old Woman who Lived in a Shoe, with all her
children. The Cat Fiddled as the Cow Jumped over the
Moon. The wheel of the old Dutch mill turned
continually. The Three Little Pigs were there, and the

Big Bad Wolf was trying to blow their house down. Jack climbed the Beanstalk. And I knew that all the Fairy Tale characters I had ever heard about were real. The wonder of it all left me enchanted forever.

# # #

In the villages throughout New Mexico, New Year's Eve was a time when family and friends gathered to celebrate the passing of the old year and the welcoming of the new. The children were allowed to stay up until midnight, while the adults ate and drank the hours away. In our family it was a time to review the happenings and accomplishments of the past year and make plans or resolutions for the year to come.

New Year's Eve was special in other ways. The young fellows in the villages hauled out a guitar or two and went from house to house, singing *Las Mañanitas,* especially if there were young ladies in the house. There were four of us teen-age girls at home and we looked forward to all this. Just imagine, being serenaded by young fellows!

My father was very strict with us, however, and since it was always midnight before the serenaders arrived at our house, he only grudgingly let them in. He fed them posole if they wanted some, and always gave them a glass of home-made wine. Then they sang again, as a way of thanking the household for the goodies, and also as a serenade to us.

"Estas son las mañanitas

que cantaba el Rey David
a las muchachas bonitas —
sí, las cantamos aquí.

"Despierta, mi bien, despierta,
mira que ya amaneció;
ya los pajarillos cantan;
la luna ya se metió. "

What a lovely way to end a day after all the cooking, baking and eating with family and friends who stopped by — to have these young fellows make you feel beautiful and special with their songs! Perhaps we have become too sophisticated for all this, but the memories are fine.

# # #

When it's chile time in New Mexico, the wonderful aroma of chile roasting up and down the streets is enough to steer you off the road or at least make you think you died and went to Heaven.

The invention of the propane chile roaster is the most wonderful invention, making life easier for the New Mexico housewife! Why it didn't merit the Nobel Prize, I'll never know!

Many long hours have been spent by the whole family, over a hot wood stove, roasting chile. In the old days we had to peel it, or sometimes we had to string it up to dry in the hot sun, in order to have green chiles in mid-winter. We hung it on the clothesline, and if it looked like rain, we brought it in, only to have to hang it up again, until it was good and dry. We stored it in tight containers. Our family did not can it, because of fear of botulism.

One late summer we were roasting chile on the wood stove in the kitchen, and the work was progressing very slowly. The fire was just not burning well, so my mother suggested that I get some wood chips to help it along. The men folks had just brought in some wood from an area in the mountains where the Forest Service was widening the road. I filled a basket with chips and started a great fire in the stove.

There were three of us in the large kitchen. My mother was at the sink and I was trying to convince my young son to play either outside or in the next room. Suddenly we were deafened by a terrible blast which destroyed the chile and the stove and left us flabbergasted. Pieces of cast iron were stuck in the ceiling, and other pieces were found thirty feet away in the living room. None of us were hurt, but the chile roasting was done for the day.

We figured it must have been a blasting cap dropped by the road workers and picked up by the wood gatherers and then by me into my basket of chips.

# # #

As children we worked hard along with our parents to sow and harvest enough food for the winter months. We learned Aesop's fable of the ant and the grasshopper, and we were no lazy grasshoppers!

"Early to bed and early to rise," must have been my mother's motto. She believed that the sun should never catch any of us in bed, and I often wondered if she believed in sleep at all.

She roused us before six in the morning, believing that the vegetables had to be gathered early in the morning before the sun dried off the dew. Then they should be canned shortly after that for best results, and she was right. But that kind of hard work before breakfast was not our idea of fun and we grumbled a lot. That didn't faze her.

Peas and green beans were the worst. She gave each of us a bucket to pick into and a basket to put them in. Handling the plants which were full of morning dew left us damp and cold. The beans she wanted us to pick were the young and tender ones, and the others were to be left on the plant to ripen. To do it right took some doing, on the part of us young and sleepy girls.

The worst part of the job was after we picked them. The shelling of the peas was extremely slow, especially if we were hungry. More went into the mouth than into the pot. We washed the beans, cut them in half, removed the stems and strings. Then they needed to be pre-cooked. I guess we didn't have a big enough kettle in which to do this, so my mother used the pressure cooker and covered them with the lid, in order to hurry the process.

One canning day a bean got stuck in the pet-cock, which is a small safety valve that releases excess steam. I'm sure our mother became pre-occupied with some other task and soon the pressure mounted. When she removed the lid, the pressure pushed boiling water, steam and green beans all over her. Her arms and chest were badly burned as she protected her face with the lid. As burned as she was she immediately looked all around to see if any of us had been burned. We weren't hurt, but we all suffered greatly anyway, because she was laid up for several weeks and we young ones had to fill in as best we could with all the household chores.

We acquired a respect for the pressure cooker which we had never had before, and it seems to me remembering now from this long perspective that it's a wonder disasters of that sort didn't happen more often.

It's different now. Most don't plant; most don't harvest; most don't can. Now you can go to the store and for very little money buy any kind of beans, either canned, frozen or fresh.

# # #

Someone asked me the other day what we did for fun in winter when we were children. We never ice-skated; we never rode a toboggan; we didn't ski. My memories of winter were mostly unpleasant. I remember being cold most of the time both at home and at school. Each child carried a piece of firewood to school, along with our books and homework, to fuel the pot-bellied stove in the middle of the schoolroom. The room was far from air-tight, and often the window panes were broken. I recall several times, when it

snowed a lot, my father bundled our feet in gunny
sacks to keep our shoes dry and our feet from getting
cold as we walked to school.

These memories have me thinking about many other
things. It only takes a question, and if you follow your
thoughts or memories, your mind can go to many
strange places. Many years later we were still fighting
the cold in winter. My husband and I read by kerosene
lamps until our eyes were weary, but for the most part
our efforts were spent trying to keep warm. We didn't
have central heating; we depended on a fireplace in the
living room and the kitchen range. I loved to cook and
bake, making good things to eat and at the same time
heating the house.

I remember one January on a bitterly cold night the
wind was blowing full blast all evening. About midnight the wind stopped. Silence can wake you up as
quickly as a sudden noise. We saw light toward the
northwest and got up to investigate, thinking of fire.
Then my husband became very excited and called me
to come see something special. I had no idea what he
meant at first. We put on our overcoats, and hurriedly
bundled up our sleepy four year old, as if fearing that
the phenomenon would instantly disappear. But it
didn't. At the time I hated waking my son, but now
I'm glad we did, because he still remembers that night,
that incredible sight! We went out into the cold, stood
on the snow-packed ground and watched the most
magnificent sky I had ever seen.

I had heard of the northern lights, but my husband's
name for it was new to me — *Aurora Borealis.*

"Aurora" means "dawn" in Spanish, but this was happening in the middle of the night. What does *"borealis"* mean? The name comes from the Roman god of the north wind. The more my husband explained the more interested I became and many more questions arose. Some he could answer and some we wondered about together.

The colored ribbons of light streaked the sky. It was like a shimmering curtain in green, blue, violet and pink bands swaying gently in the breeze. I found out later that the aurora appears at both magnetic poles and that the colors and brilliance depend on where you are, what time it is and what is happening on the Sun. An aurora is caused by atomic particles from the Sun, called the Solar Wind, striking the atmospheric gases, above the earth's magnetic field. I have never seen one again, although there was one seen here in 1991. I didn't know it at the time and am sorry I missed it.

# # #

One spring we almost missed the most important thing going on in our back yard. As we sat in the back porch we noticed a hummingbird who seemed quite unhappy about our being there. It acted as if it were waiting for us to leave so it could get its work done. A day or so later we realized she was building a nest over a conduit pipe at the porch ceiling.

We wished we had noticed earlier and watched the whole process, for the finished product was really very artistic. She had found very thin strips of paper and

other material and fastened the nest to the conduit pipe
by somehow gluing the strips from the top to the
bottom of the nest. Shortly after that we noticed two
tiny beaks showing, one on each side of the nest. The
nest was so tiny that we couldn't imagine how the two
little ones could fit in it.

We climbed up on the picnic table, with a hand
mirror at the ceiling, in order to see two tiny blobs in
the nest. The beak was the largest part of each tiny
body. The mother no longer cared if we were around,
for she had work to do. She fed them and at night slept
outside the nest as if watching over them.

Then one day, as we watched, one of the
hummingbirds flew out of the nest and just a few
inches away onto the pipe. He called out, "Weee-weee-
weee," as he practiced flying up near the ceiling. Then
he scooted out of the porch and away, never to return.
A day later the other bird flew away and it too never
came back to the nest. How different from human
children!

# # #

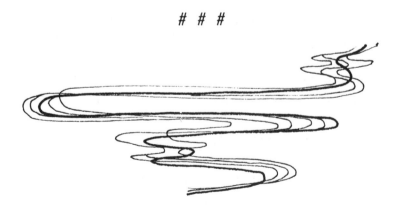

A few years ago my sister Lina was moving from New York on her way to San Francisco and spent several days here with us. I was trying to be a good hostess by preparing foods which she enjoyed. She asked me to make her some *biscochitos,* which I was glad to do. We had been away from each other so many years that we had much to share. There were happy memories and many sad ones, so between tears and laughter, phone calls and someone at the door, I tried to cook and bake.

The first batch of cookies came out of the oven as she poured our cups of coffee. She took one bite and made an awful face. I wondered what had gone wrong with my wonderful recipe. In the midst of all the commotion I had inadvertently used salt in place of sugar. We threw away the first batch and the rest of the dough. The birds refused them and I'm sure the worms in the compost pit did not appreciate that dough either.

Later in the week after coming home from work, I wondered out loud what we should fix for dinner. I proposed some complicated and time-consuming recipe, but Lina came up with what I thought was a bright idea. She said, "Listen, you know, and I know, that we are both good cooks, in spite of that *biscochito* catastrophe! We don't have to prove anything to anyone, so let's go out and get us a hamburger." We did that and rented a video and thoroughly enjoyed the evening.

# # #

Borrachita me voy, para olvidarle —
Le quiero mucho, él también me quiere.
Borrachita me voy, hasta la capital,
Pa' servir al patrón que me mandó llamar
anteayer.   — Mexican Folk Song

My first experience with wine occurred many years ago, while traveling in Spain by train from Barcelona to Madrid on *"El Talgo."* My husband and I had decided not to have dinner until we arrived in Madrid, but when we saw what the waiters were bringing to passengers who ordered *la cena,* we decided to order also. They fitted a wooden tray to our seat, and brought each of us a loaf of bread and a small bottle of red wine. I was flabbergasted to think that this entire bottle of wine was for me!

We could see that dinner was going to consist of many courses, but there was also plenty of delay. So — we started in on the bread, and the wine. At first the wine seemed sour to me, but as I ate the bread, and got used to the wine, I thought it was great. By the time the rest of the dinner came along, the bread and wine were gone and I was happily singing, *"Borrachita me voy."* In the song the young woman is lamenting having to leave her lover behind in order to obey *el patrón...*

# # #

We live by the side of the road, where the race of man goes by, so every now and then someone stops for a morsel of bread. A couple came to the door one miserably cold evening and asked for something to eat. I served them the *posol* which was to have been our dinner, and with it tortillas and hot coffee. They seemed satisfied, but to make the meal complete I served them some poppy seed cake.

As they ate, I remembered something from my childhood. At one time my family lived in a small town beside the railroad. During the Depression the so-called "hobos" stopped to ask for food. If I remember correctly, we ourselves were poor, but we always had beans and bread or tortillas.

One time a "gringo" hobo asked for butter, after my folks had given him bread. My father was appalled at the request, for I don't think he himself was sure what butter looked like in those times! He had a saying after that: *"El hombre blanco tiene que tener algo para poner en su pan."* [The white man must always have something to spread on his bread.] To this day, I want my family to eat the bread alone and really know what it tastes like without camouflaging it with spreads.

I found myself watching the reaction of our visitors that cold night to the special poppy-seed cake I had placed before them. The man ate his piece without hesitation, but the woman began to pick out each tiny seed and place it on the table. Soon she became discouraged and simply left the cake on the plate. I wonder what she thought the seeds were, or where they came from.

# # #

Some memories are painful, but they come back anyway. I call them "hard memories." Maybe they make us into what we really are, what makes us unique.

Sometime in the early 1930's a traveling salesman from Stark Brothers Nursery came into our village and sold fruit trees to my father. We ended up with some cherry, peach and plum trees, and a beautiful apple orchard which helped provide part of our family income.

The fruits ripened at different times, and we youngsters sold them from a roadside stand to tourists. The apples were the main crop, and our family traded them for things we needed. We traded with the Pueblos, apples for feed grain and blue corn meal. We traded with itinerant vendors, apples for school shoes and winter clothing. We traded at the mercantile, apples for other supplies we did not grow ourselves. And what was left over for ourselves lasted until after Christmas.

The apple orchard was a magical place, especially at apple blossom time. We played among the butterflies,

the clover, the bees, and we imagined ourselves in a
heavenly world. In the fall we helped with the picking
— it was the only time we were allowed to climb the
trees, and then only barefoot or with tennis shoes, so
as not to injure the trees. I remember how my father
painted over any scratch, to keep the tree from losing
sap.

Then the State Highway Department came to our
village, widening and paving the road. To keep the
road straight, they took a large corner of the property
and almost the entire orchard. The beautiful trees were
priced from five to fifteen dollars each; the family
received a total of some three hundred dollars for the
orchard. My father wept. It seems unreal, as I think
back. The orchard was ruined, pride was gone, and the
few trees left were neglected. Sad memories come
back to me, whenever I smell apple blossoms.

# # #

As a very young child, I loved to sew. Making doll
clothes and other simple things such as potholders, to
please my mother, was the most fun. At first I sewed
by hand, but that was slow and tedious and early on I
graduated myself to the old treadle sewing machine.
All went well until I passed the needle through my
finger. My mother was very upset, and for a long time
I was not allowed to use the machine.

Leafing through a Christmas catalog I found and
coveted a little red sewing machine. I dreamed Santa
Claus would surely bring it to me. No one told me that

he would, and no one promised me anything; but I just assumed that if I wished hard enough, it would happen.

Years went by, and when I came home for Christmas after my first year at boarding school, I found the little red sewing machine waiting for me. That year I had taken Home Economics and had made myself my first dress on a professional adult sewing machine. I was totally surprised when my mother handed me the gift. I doubt very much if I even thanked her for at least the effort in acquiring it and I'll never know how disappointed she must have been for not pleasing me. For me it was like dredging some memory or desire from the distant past. It was no longer important!

I went back to school for three and one half more years and never thought about it again. I left the gift at home so the younger children would play with it, and don't know what happened to it. Sometimes we stand still and time passes us by, and at other times, time seems to stand still and we pass it by. Such irony!

# # #

My recent visit to the large weaving room at El Rito, with rows of looms and people weaving on some of them, reminded me of years gone by, when I, too, was a weaver, albeit, for a very short period of time. It was with Burro Weavers situated in Burro Alley in Santa Fe. I had learned weaving with a young man from La Madera and this was my first job.

I think back and can't imagine how I did it then and why I would ever do it again. The owner was an old, old man with a cane, who walked back and forth between the aisles watching closely each worker. When he thought we weren't fast enough or found us correcting a mistake, he banged the side of the loom with his cane and scared us half to death. He did this one time to me and I got so scared that I shoved the shuttle so hard that it went all the way through the warp and down the other side and down onto the floor. He kept hitting the side of the loom upsetting me so much that it was impossible for me to do anything right.

Luckily I quit at the end of the week. Talk about a slave master and sweat shops, we've had them here. We worked eight hours a day and forty hours a week for five dollars a week. Just think, I was fourteen years old and worked for 12 ½ cents an hour. It was the going wage then.

# # #

Have you ever tried to clean a *ristra* of dry red chile? The experience will be more than you bargained for. I missed the adventure as a child, because my mother always had a woman help her clean and grind two or three ristras at once every fall. We children were not expected to help. The women divided the ground chile between them.

After I got married my husband decided that the only way to get pure chile was to do it ourselves, and he

was right. The packaged chile available in stores at
that time was always mixed with ground dried peas to
make it stretch further, providing more profit. There
is such a thing as progress — we seldom find
adulterated chile these days, but things were different
then.

My husband and I started the process by removing
the pods from the strings that held them together to
dry, but that was just the beginning. By the time we
finished that first step, he washed up and disappeared
and I realized the job was mine. I cleaned the pods by
scraping the seeds and veins with a paring knife.
Remember, that's one chile pod at a time! I could feel
the dry chile dust on my hands, in my nose and eyes.
It spread throughout my whole body. I stopped to get
myself a cup of coffee and rest from the ordeal, but as
I washed my hands, I inadvertently scratched my ear,
and then my arms, and found that I had more areas on
fire.

After the coffee break, I placed the pods in a pan of
water, to wash away all the dust that had accumulated
during the drying period. I removed them to a cookie
sheet and into the warm oven to dry. I had to be
careful that the oven was not too hot, or else the chile
would darken and have a burnt taste. But it had to be
entirely dry, in order to grind easily. In my
inexperience that took hours. My body was burning
and I was angry that I had been left alone with this
miserable job. Finally, when the pods were all dry, I
set up my old-fashioned meat grinder, and ground
them to a fine powder.

When the job was finished I burned for 24 hours. With no shower in the house, taking a bath only spread the burning all over my body, from head to toe. I understood the word enchilada in a new way. In Spanish we would say, *"¡Estoy enchilada!"* meaning, "I'm full of red chile dust and burning all over!" I felt just like a hot enchilada, and swore that if I had to clean another *ristra,* I would never eat red chile again!

# # #

When I was first married, I wanted so much to please my husband that I decided to make him an apple pie. I had heard that the way to a man's heart was through his stomach and I knew he loved pies. I tried to remember how my mother made them, but had never really watched her closely. The fruit was cooked with sugar over the stove, while she made the pie crust. Naturally, I tried the same trick — "monkey see, monkey do." I cooked the apples with sugar until they were nearly dead, while I made the pie crust. I made it more or less the same way I made tortilla dough, with a little more shortening and too much baking powder, without measuring anything.

Results: apple-tortilla mish-mash. I presented the pie for dinner. My husband took a look and said nothing. I waited. When he bit into it, he said, "Never bake a pie without using a recipe."

I tried to defend myself by saying, "I made it like my mother makes them."

He gently said, "That doesn't mean she makes good

pies."

I was not angry, just terribly embarrassed for not knowing any better. My Home Economics teacher had given me THE AMERICAN COOKBOOK as a graduation gift, which I had never opened. I guess I thought it was to be saved on a shelf. Next day I opened the cookbook and realized how far I was from making a good pie. The embarrassment and shame I had gone through taught me to read recipes carefully, and I learned with a vengeance.

# # #

# # #

Old or Young.
I do not know if I am young or old.
Age does not determine that question entirely.
It has to do with how I feel, and what I do with each day.

I am in many ways old-fashioned.

I have values which belong to a past generation.

I am not an ideal consumer of goods — much advertising is wasted on me. I buy only what I need.

I don't like calling attention to myself — I was taught that children should be seen and not heard.

I no longer jump up and run, or climb, or fall gracefully without breaking bones. I have learned.

I rest when I need to. I read, I listen, I think.

I have my house remodeled, adding more light here and easier access there. I eliminate kitchen gadgets which I seldom or never use.

I simplify.

On the other hand, I am still young.

I love games — word games, railroad games, Acquire®, and Upwords® are my favorites. I will drop whatever I am doing, when the opportunity comes up for a game. I am a good loser, but I also love to win.

I am still game to climb, when I think it's worth the effort. Late in life I climbed Teotihuacán, Cobá and Chichén-Itzá.

Recently I climbed almost a mile of uneven, rocky path, 271 steps, several tunnels, unlit bunkers and a dark spiral staircase to the top of Diamond Head in Hawaii, with a broken foot! I kept up with the young people for five days, including a noisy evening at Planet Hollywood! I enjoy life to the fullest.

# # #

Early morning, the smell of early fall,
Doing Tai Chih exercises in the back patio,
Watching the clouds go by — hurricanes far away,
The hummingbirds feeding, preparing for their long
flight,
Mourning doves coming around for hand-out
breakfast —
The garden still gives of its beauty.
Sweet peas, four o'clocks, fall sage, princess
feather, even a canna lily surprises me.
The trees look sad — their leaves no longer shine.
Summer is gone.
Fall is here, and it is time to rest.
Sunflowers looked me happily in the face
yesterday;
today they are withered and looking sad.
A time to ponder one's own time to rest.
It will come when least expected.
No one is ever really, really ready!

# # #

It is our inward journey that leads us through time.
We go forward and backward, but seldom in a
straight line.
We are moving, changing, with respect to others.
As we discover, we remember.
As we remember, we discover.

# # #

Things lost — or are they hiding from me?
A beautiful cross on a gold chain, given to me from Hawaii long ago, the first gift from a boyfriend.
Lost, lost.
Found later in the lace part of an old brassiere.

Great recipes lost, where filed?
Under the name of the one who gave it to me, of course.
Why would I do it right?
My filing is lousy.

A twenty-dollar bill,
found in an old purse, ready to be cast away.
I could have spent it may times for food,
but it hid from me, until one day when I didn't need it.

Thoughts move in the mind faster and more fully than can be expressed.
When not written down, they slip away, fly away, but sometimes return, when I really need them.
Not always.

# # #

Man's life span has often been compared to flowers, or "the grass of the field," but mostly to the seasons. We've heard people say that some young person is in the Spring of his or her life, or that an older person is in the Winter of his or her life. For some of us, we are entering the October of our lives, some early Fall, some late Fall. With this awareness comes a certain feeling of sadness, resigned to enjoy what time there is left. Lucky for me that I have a lifetime of memories which I treasure and recall every chance I get. No, we don't need to live in the past, but we need to nourish ourselves with past joys and life's richness.

There is also a funny side to this stage of life. We hate being reminded of our birthdays, as if we could capture time and hold back the years. We do not like to be helped in and out of the car. We are perfectly capable of doing it ourselves! We avoid any of the gadgets which will be of great help and even necessary later on, such as some kind of grab bar in the bathtub. We resist the idea that we might need a hearing aid, and accuse others of mumbling.

We purposely buy a house with stairs which later on we won't be able to climb. We insist on walking ten blocks instead of being dropped in front of the meeting house, just to prove we can still do it. We claim that the walk will do us good even if we're out of breath by the time we get to where we're going. If our children suggest a five mile hike, we take them up on it, just as if we had good sense. We live in self-denial to the bitter end!

# # #

A couple of years ago we went to one of the pueblos to visit our friends and enjoy the feast day. We enjoyed a wonderful noon-day meal, and then went to the plaza. It was early afternoon on a very hot summer day. We leaned against an adobe wall at the far end of the plaza to watch the dancers. We talked with other visitors to the pueblo, and discussed all the different ceremonies we had attended in several pueblos. Then we became spellbound by the throbbing of the drums, the chanting of the chorus, and the steady beat of the feet of the dancers. We could see a shrine of freshly cut evergreens and flowers at the far end of the plaza. The colorful dress of the women and the lines of half-naked men passed before us. We stood there transfixed by it all.

After a while we realized that the intense rays of the sun were getting the best of us. The vibrations, made up of drumbeats, steady hypnotic feet movements, chanting, bells and gourd rattles, combined with our own pulse, left us a bit confused. We tried to continue to enjoy and endure but the discomfort was too great. As we asked each other how we felt, we began to fear sunstroke. We gave it up and left. We had been foolish enough to go without hats or an umbrella, even though we had just been through that hard stretch of summer, days and days of dry, 100-degree weather.

On the drive home we remembered the song that Joan Baez wrote and sang years ago, entitled, *"What Have They Done to the Rain?"* Our experience made us wonder what we as a species had done to the *sun.* As children both of us had spent hours in the sun without a worry about sunstroke or skin cancer. Now we are being told constantly to think of the sun as our enemy. We had never paid very much attention to this alarm, until this experience with the sun in the pueblo.

# # #

My mother lived alone for almost forty years after my father died, and in the late stages felt that friends and family did not come often enough to visit her. She sang a song when she was young and repeated it to us as she got older, when the song had even more meaning. The song went like this:

Así es el árbol cuando está de hojas copado,
Todos se acercan a su sombra a descansar.
Llega el invierno; llega a quedar deshojado,
Ni quien se acuerde que ha llegado allí a sombrear.

She compared the life of a person to a tree in its summer fullness, where a traveler would stop to rest and enjoy its magnificent shade. Then when winter arrived and the tree dropped its leaves, people passed by without remembering they had ever rested there. Of course, this had more meaning in her day, when a man going from field to field on foot with a shovel or hoe over his shoulder, sought the shade of a tree.

She lived in a house by the side of the road, where people passing by could always find a bowl of chile and beans, or posole. She never understood that people sometimes move away, and often begin new lives apart from those they knew before. Some have problems which they do not wish to share with old friends. Some old friends die. We tried to make her understand this, but through it all there was no denying, her song rang true.

# # #

In our village there was an elderly man who lived close by and often visited with my parents. He was a good neighbor and he and my father often worked together on farm projects. We liked to sit and listen to the stories he told of when he was a boy. He told how sharp-eyed he was, and how he used to be able to see a deer at a great distance when hunting with his father. He did not complain of any aches and pains in his aging body, but he often said, *"El mundo es muy opaco. "* [The world is very opaque.]

As a child I wondered what he meant. He used the word *es*, as if meaning, "unchangeable." He should have used *está*, for the condition was not permanent. In fact it wasn't a condition of the world at all. He was projecting onto the world what was going on within him. *Opaco* was not out there, but in his vision. To him bright colors had become pale and objects faint. Now, as I get older and have eye problems of my own, I begin to understand what he meant.

# # #

Those of us who grew up during World War II experienced rationing, which enabled everyone to share in the little that was available. We could buy some necessities, when they were in the stores, but only if we had the ration stamps. The stamps were doled out so that each individual or family received a fair share.

My parents were the only ones who drank coffee at

home (it was not for children, they said), so we had extra coffee stamps and often exchanged them for sugar with other families in the village. Honey was a fine substitute for those of us who had a bee hive.

The children went barefoot all summer, which was a blessing. Non-rationed "play-shoes," as they were called, were made of cardboard and disintegrated with normal use in a very short time, and when wet fell apart immediately. The ration stamps for shoes were used by the males, who worked the farm or were employed outside the home.

Can you imagine making a Mexican meal without lard, or any other kind of shortening? We made tortillas with mayonnaise in place of lard and they were good, but they turned hard as crackers shortly after they were made.

Horse meat became available once more as it had been during the depression. When a family butchered a calf or pig in the village, they would sell part of it or exchange for something you had and they needed, like honey or eggs.

Gasoline was not a big problem in a poor village, for few people had a car and certainly only one car to a family. And where was there to go? Families were scattered. The men folks were in the military services and many of the women, young and old, went to work in defense plants, mostly on the West Coast.

The natives here in New Mexico depended mostly on what they grew and the livestock they raised. It was a simple life. Beans, chile and the like were the mainstay. Besides these we had chickens and plenty of eggs. I learned to make omelettes out of almost any vegetable. Our favorite was the asparagus and potato omelette. Onions and garlic grew well and as seasoning they can't be beat.

# # #

For a couple of years we were dissatisfied with our flower garden, because the perennials, like iris and oriental poppies, were no longer doing well, and the annuals, including larkspur and cosmos, were only sparsely reseeding themselves. The soil was becoming too hard for anything to do well, and the garden had taken on the appearance of confusion without beauty. Last fall we plowed everything under, removing bulbs and perennials, leaving only trees and large shrubs.

We were pleasantly surprised by how we felt about the results. Our yard seemed bigger than we remembered, and the open space gave us new ideas for keeping a clear view of the larger picture. We added compost and turned it over several times. We replanted the spring bulbs in October. In the spring when it was almost time to finish replanting, we found ourselves hesitating, fearing that once again we could overcrowd the area, and lose the feeling of openness which we liked so much.

I marvel at how easy it is to crowd or fill in any empty space we find, whether in our gardens, our closets, our homes, or our lives. For example, we think we need more table space, but as soon as we get another desk, immediately it is covered over with magazines, books and papers. It takes a lot of courage to do away with anything, or even to change things a little bit.

We watched a TV special some time back, named *"Affluenza. "* At first I thought it meant influenza — a serious epidemic, due to the influence of the stars, or a highly contagious virus. To my surprise affluenza is an entirely new word, with a different meaning altogether. It is derived from our affluent society, and its symptoms are overwork, stress, unnecessary shopping, and debt. It was interesting how the TV show called this an epidemic, which they claimed was the cause of psychological depression as well as depletion of the purse. They even called it a plague, with a high rate of mortality.

Just as we overloaded our flower garden with more than the soil could possibly maintain, we tend to crowd all aspects of our lives. Some of our purchases are things we need. Most are things we thought were bargains. The habit of buying is so strong in our society that it enables builders to erect more and more spaces in which we can store the results of our incredible buying habit. We buy when we are sad, when we are lonely, because we have the money, because we saw the ad on TV, or because we have a place to store it just in case we need it some day. There are so many reasons for hoarding, that we can truly call it a contagious disease or an epidemic.

I have at one time or another fallen into this trap, only to find that bargains are seldom really bargains, seldom less expensive in the long run than what I usually buy, and nearly always something I could do without.

Some of the stories I hear from family and friends make me chuckle. People speak of their refrigerators and freezers being so full that they have a difficult time deciding what to prepare for dinner — so they go out to eat, or buy something else already prepared. Our kitchens are so full of gadgets, which are seldom used, and when needed cannot be found — so we go out and buy more gadgets. Closets are so full of clothing that we complain we have nothing to wear — so we go out and buy one more special outfit for that special occasion. Simplicity is the key to all this, but we have lost or misplaced it.

# # #

I am floating over a troubled world,
seeking a safe and peaceful place.
  Where will I go to find this?
  Perhaps there is no such place.
  Only in the private sector of my life,
  Exploring my inner journey —
  Recalling memories which are both
exciting and nourishing —
  Time past and time present flowing together,
exploring possibilities within myself.

  A passion for growing,
which is necessary and never-ending —
  Seeking new adventures, and taking risks —

Knowing that home is where
the real things of life are sown and reaped, and
where in the end the real things happen.
   Where partners live and try to grow together —
   A partner who will help push a little at risk time
and be there to pick up the pieces when failure
comes.

   I want to gather the parts of me
that I have hidden away.
   How did I know I would need them and have to
find them?
   Hoarding energy like a miser for tomorrow.
   Who knows what surprise may come to demand it?
   Life contains unforeseen undercurrents,
good and bad.

   I hardly recognize myself at age twenty, thirty or
even forty. I smile and continue.
   I must lose all fear of change,
for I know it is coming.
   I must share my humanity, my aging,
my mortality.
   I am learning to appreciate and value
the only companion I will always have — myself.

# # #

Related Books
from
AMADOR PUBLISHERS:

TWELVE GIFTS
Recipes from a Southwest Kitchen
by
Adela Amador

"'Twas the twelfth day of Christmas
and my true love gave to me:
twelve sopaipillas,
eleven empanadas,
ten biscochitos..."

MORE GIFTS
With Variations

Thirteen more recipes from Adela's
Kitchen, including Paella, Sopa and
Rhubarb Pie.
Adela Amador has been feeding
the multitudes for many decades from her
house by the side of the road. Here she
shares some of her miracles.

The Little Brown Roadrunner

LITTLE BROWN ROADRUNNER
who did it herself

"If you want a job done, assign it to a busy person."

"If you want a job done right, do it yourself."

"If you want a helping hand, you'll find the best one at the end of your wing."

Here Little Brown Roadrunner learns these valuable lessons. Some of us have heard them before, from Little Red Hen, but when that story reached the Great Southwest, this is how it came out.

Claiborne O'Connor's illustrations provide a whimsical counterpoint for **Leon Wender's** straightforward text.

"Small children will delight in this book. The illustrations are lots of fun. The print is big and simple and many kids can read it themselves. They can even color the illustrations if they want to."
— NEW MEXICO MAGAZINE

SOUTHWEST!

CAESAR OF SANTA FE
A Novel from History
by Tim MacCurdy
ISBN: 0-938513-07-9 [240 pp. $11.95]

This rousing tale describes the administration of Governor Luís de Rosas, in colonial New Mexico around 1640. A tempestuous love affair determines, temporarily, the outcome of a bitter struggle for power between government officials and Catholic missionary/clergy.

Tim MacCurdy is a literary historian and critic. He has published fifteen books of criticism, while teaching Spanish language and literature for 32 years at the University of New Mexico. This story is well-researched; to understand this period, one can molder in the archives, or enjoy this novel.

PRIZE-WINNER! Best First Novel, 1991 -- WESTERN WRITERS OF AMERICA

"Tim MacCurdy combines an intimate knowledge of New Mexico history and a story teller's still in this remarkable novel. It should become one of our classics."
          -- Tony Hillerman, author of A THIEF OF TIME

"...the product of impeccable research... Seventeenth century Santa Fe springs fully to life... leaves the reader with the feeling that he, too, was there."   -- THE TEXAS REVIEW

"New Mexico's mountains, deserts and isolated communities, reeking with old Spanish tradition and Indian folklore... MacCurdy displays a keen intelligence and sense of irony... an astute observer of the vagaries of human character... superstition, ignorance, power struggle, cruelty, violence... wry humor suffused with tragedy and pity. MacCurdy delights in and delights us with the often raucous life of early New Mexico."   -- THE SANTA FE NEW MEXICAN

"MacCurdy is a wonderful teacher and an author of exquisite quality."
          -- THE ALBUQUERQUE TRIBUNE

"Santa Fe of 1640, with whipping post and Inn of the Humpbacked Cat, comes to lusty, brawling life in this story of conflict between Governor Luís de Rosas and the priests who were nearly all, according to MacCurdy, engaged in exploiting and alienating the Indians. Rosas falls in love with a married woman, which exacerbates the hostility between peninsular Spaniards and criollos. Excellent detail and believable people."   -- BOOKS OF THE SOUTHWEST

"The novel is quick and entertaining reading, giving insight into the clandestine activities of Governor Luís de Rosas and his cronies, whose exploits are chronicled in existing judicial and ecclesiastical records from that period... packed full of liaisons, class consciousness, witchcraft, warfare and a varied cast of characters."   -- NEW MEXICO MAGAZINE

CROSSWINDS
A Darkly Comic Modern Western
by Michael A. Thomas
ISBN: 0-938513-02-8 [169 pp. $8]

A young construction worker with low impulse control struggles to be a sane hard-working citizen, exposing the duplicities of modern society, which crush all that is unique and genuine from the old rural values.

Michael Thomas was born in Raton and reared in Alamogordo, New Mexico, near ground zero of the world's first atom bomb blast. His ambition to become a surfer was difficult to achieve in New Mexico. Today he is an anthropologist, counselor and teacher.

"Novels set in Eastern New Mexico are rare...really good ones even more so! The droll language reaches into our unrecognized prejudices and false fronts and drags them jolting into the light of a marijuana bonfire. A superb writer has found his way onto the list of a budding New Mexico publisher. Both are to be congratulated."
— BOOKTALK

"Very funny, very convincing novel of the Great Southwest, with accurate and nicely-drawn characters. It would make a good movie, though I'd hate to lose the dry, Ring Lardner-style narration."
— ALBUQUERQUE JOURNAL MAGAZINE

"The book exudes the Southwestern ambience, celebrating the land, the people and the language. The characters include several strong women, red-necks, ex-hippies, wetbacks and fundamentalists. The undercurrents of meaning beneath the surface of this joyful and amusing story are notable."
— THE RATON RANGE

"This blue-collar novel is concerned with current moral problems such as ecology and racial discrimination."
— BOOKS OF THE SOUTHWEST

"CROSSWINDS reminds me of so many people I know. For all his craziness the hero has a sensitivity to people and the environment. He is a real New Mexican, and I haven't seen this character in literature before. He's from 'the other New Mexico.'"
— Denise Chavez, author of THE LAST MENU GIRLS

"...a big marijuana stash, put-upon wetback laborers, a batch of ornery people and sundry 'shenanigans, complications and stratagems'...the development of the narrator from a foul-mouthed adolescent into a worthwhile human being..."

-- NEW MEXICO MAGAZINE

DUKE CITY TALES
STORIES FROM ALBUQUERQUE
by Harry Willson
ISBN: 0-938513-00-0 [176 pp. $9]

Luminarias, balloons, atomic bombs, bats, false arrest, hunting, finding, moonwatching, DWI, cops, schools, litter, mufflers, stray dogs, and a fumbling old alchemist, who attempts to use his occult powers to bring about his goal of "peace and quiet," with results that are comical and less than satisfactory, giving pause to those of us who feel called upon to change the world.

"Duke City" is Albuquerque -- the commercial, educational, medical, military metropolis that contains half the population of New Mexico. Harry Willson, has lived there more than thirty years as a practicing mythologist and story-teller.

"Willson's keen insight into human nature is intermingled cleverly within the stories' events, revealing both the stupid and the serious, the touching and the absurd, leaving the reader feeling that he has just been exposed to a truth that he has sensed before, but which for the first time is verbalized." — THE SMALL PRESS REVIEW

SOULS AND CELLS REMEMBER:
A LOVE STORY
by H. G. Z. Willson

ISBN: 0-938513-03-6 [188 pp. $8]

a tender love story
full of anger and ancient longings,
cultural/racial confrontation
and reincarnation,
moving in place
from New Mexico to the Susquehanna,
and in time
from the present to the 1750's
and back...

"Journeying across the continent from West to East and across two centuries in time, protagonists Thomas Grady and Flora Esperante confront ancestral images, hostility, sex, outward anger and inner reality. According to my friends who know, the white teacher and the Native American potter accurately introduce readers to the fascinating realm of metaphysics." — BOOKS OF THE SOUTHWEST

"A dream you would like to have come true for yourself." — Silver Ravenwolf

AMADOR PUBLISHERS
P. O. Box 12335
Albuquerque, NM 87195
Phone/FAX 505-877-4395
To Order: 800-730-4395
e-mail   harry@amadorbooks.com
http://www.amadorbooks.com

ORDER BLANK

of copies   price

_____ UNDERCURRENTS   @ 12.00 _____
_____ TWELVE GIFTS   @ 4.00 _____
_____ MORE GIFTS   @ 4.00 _____
_____ DUKE CITY TALES   @ 9.00 _____
_____ THE LITTLE BROWN
                  ROADRUNNER   @ 4.00 _____
_____ CAESAR OF SANTA FE   @ 12.00 _____
_____ SOULS AND CELLS
                  REMEMBER   @ 8.00 _____
_____ CROSSWINDS   @ 8.00 _____

                  postage & handling   2.00

                  Total
                                                    _____

Send to: Name_____

          Address_____

          City, State, Zip_____